The ABC's of Sexual Assault

Anatomy, "Bunk" and the Courtroom

The ABC's of Sexual Assault

Anatomy,
"Bunk"
and the Courtroom

Michelle Ditton RN, SANE-A, SANE-P
Laurie A. Gray, JD

Socratic Parenting LLC

SOCRATIC PARENTING LLC
Published by Socratic Parenting LLC
Fort Wayne, Indiana, U.S.A.
www.SocraticParenting.com
Copyright © Socratic Parenting LLC, 2015

Paperback: 978-0-9864471-9-8
Electronic Book: 978-0-9864471-0-5

Socratic Parenting LLC

Dedication

For Steve
I wouldn't have missed the dance!

For Stefanie & Ashley
I thank you with all of my heart for understanding.
I love you more.

~MD

To Karen Richards, Pat Smallwood,
Fran Gull and Kim Churchward
for showing me how to make a difference.

~LG

To all those whom our justice system has failed
and to all who've dedicated their professional lives to
making sure it works.

~ MD & LG

Table of Contents

Acknowledgments

We wish to express the deepest gratitude to Dr. Joyce Adams for her input regarding the medical content in this book and for writing the Foreword.

To the FWSATC forensic nurses, colleagues and friends, Leslie Cook, Joyce Moss, Angela Mellon, Shawn Callahan, and Sara Coburn: You are each uniquely different, yet all of you heal souls and change lives. The words "thank you" can never be enough, but THANK YOU for making a difference. We are especially indebted for your assistance in compiling and reviewing the information in this book.

For their assistance in editing our earliest drafts, many thanks to Frank Gray, Louise Magoon, Nancy Smith, Diane Witwer and Tami Zehr.

We also recognize and appreciate the following people for reading early versions of the book and providing valuable suggestions and comments: Cheryl Brockman, Michelle Corrao, Lee Craine, Dottie Davis, Sara Drury, Tony Geller, Patty Harting, Gayle Keane, Jim Luttrull, Neil Moore, Kristin Morris, Gary O'Connor, Robin Pfeiffer, Peter Ransbottom, Judie Scott, Deb Sanchez, Beth Shaw, Paul Shrawder, Stacey Speith, Tina Taviano, AmyMarie Travis, Peggy Virgil, and Deborah Zehr.

Special thanks to Marilyn Grundy and Julie Kenniston who encouraged us to develop and present much of the information in this book at the National Symposium on Child Abuse in Huntsville, Alabama, from 2009 through 2014, and to Gary O'Connor and Paul Tressler for watching Michelle present at the National Symposium and inviting her to work with Fox Valley Technical College and present at the Missing and Exploited Children Conference and for the Office of Juvenile Justice and Delinquency Prevention.

We are grateful to the following physicians for their ongoing support and reading advanced review copies of the book: Alex Antalis, Pramod Carpenter, Marv Eastlund, Kathryn Einhaus, Susan Frayer, Eamonn Keane, Andy O'Shaughnessy, and Peter

Rothman. Thank you to Paul Blusys for first introducing Michelle and Laurie back in 2000, and the rest is history.

There are no words to express our gratitude for those who have believed in SANEs and made it possible for us at the FWSATC to do what we do. Without Bob Gevers and Neil Moore there would be no Fort Wayne Sexual Assault Treatment Center. Tony Geller and Stacey Speith encouraged us, taught us about the legal system, and prepared us to testify with confidence. Without Rich Miller and Joe Zehr's wisdom and guidance we would not have survived the storms. Thank you to Robin Pfeiffer for always having our back. Thank you to Tami Zehr for reminding us that no matter how we feel, "Get up. Dress up. Show up. And never give up."

We are humbled by all those who have paved the way for this journey: Mike Burris, Frank Byrne, Dan Garman, Kathryn Garner, Kathryn Einhaus, Judy Elwell, Geray Farrell, Jamie Ferrell, Tom Gutwein, Pat Harper, Roberta Hibbard, Diane Hopen, Rich Kaplan, Bill Lewis, Jeannie Longsworth, Phillip O'Shaughnessy, Ron Rayl, Amy Richison, Craig Robison, Brian Sell, Paul Shrawder, Joe Squadrito, Scott Wagner, and John Zagelmeier. We appreciate the sound legal counseling provided by Mark Bloom and Holly Brady and the fundraising efforts of Jim and Cheryl Brockman, Denise and David DeMarchis, Judy and Ross Elwell, Cathy Fisher, Lorrie Freiburger, Kayla Henderson, Lynette Holiday, Matilda Jane, Andy and Robin Pfeiffer, Peter Rothman, Marilyn and Mike Stanford, and Deborah and Ric Zehr. You truly are the heartbeat of the Center.

A special thank you to our mothers, Judie Scott and Peggy Virgil, and our best friends, Gabrielle Cutino and Beth Shaw.

We are honored to make this information available to all those who may benefit from it.

Foreword

The sexual assault of children, adolescents and adults is widespread in the United States and the world. It is not a new problem, but the approach to patients/victims by the medical-legal community has evolved and improved over the last decade.

The incidence of sexual assault in the United States is disturbingly high. A nationally representative survey conducted in 2010, reported the following statistics:

- Overall, approximately 1 in 5 women (18.3%) and 1 in 71 men (1.4%) reported ever having been raped
- 42.2% of female rape victims reported first rape at <18 years of age
- 12.3% of female and 27.8% of male victims reported first rape at less than 11 years of age
- 19% of college women reported attempted or completed rape since starting college
- 11.8% of high school girls and 4.5% of high school boys reported having experienced a forced sexual encounter

(http://www.cdc.gov/violenceprevention/sexualviolence/datasourc es.html).[1] Clearly, sexual assault respects no age barriers. Because rape is so common, it is essential for victims of all ages to have access to high quality medical care and legal assistance.

In the medical community, nurses have taken on the primary burden for performing the forensic examination and treatment of adolescent and adult victims of sexual assault. Physicians, especially in hospital Emergency Departments, are usually happy to have a qualified nurse conduct these evaluations. The American Board of Pediatrics recognized a new subspecialty of Child Abuse Pediatrics and the first group of physicians became certified in the subspecialty in 2009, but some physicians had been providing care to child victims of sexual abuse for decades prior to this certification.

The medical evaluation and care of children who may have been sexually abused requires a specific set of knowledge and skills, and also requires continuing education in this field of medicine. One of the things that my colleagues and I do most often when teaching others about the sexual abuse examination is to dispel the many myths about the child's body and how it reacts to sexual molestation and rape. This book will be a great tool for all the members of the multidisciplinary team that work with victims of assault and their families to explain and challenge those myths.

Many people, inside and outside the medical field do not understand the basics of female genital anatomy. The first section of this book describes the anatomy of both males and females, emphasizing that in contrast to the prevalent myth, the hymen in an adolescent girl or an adult woman can stretch to allow penetration by an object the size of a penis without tearing. It is a very entrenched myth in our culture and many others, that the hymen always tears the first time a girl has vaginal intercourse.

The results of one important study by Kellogg, et al[2] should have dispelled this myth about the hymen once and for all, but apparently it has not done so. Dr. Kellogg and her colleagues reviewed magnified photographs of the hymen of pregnant adolescent girls and found that evidence of a previous tear to the hymen was demonstrated in only 6% of the girls. The estrogen produced by the body of a woman who has gone through puberty causes the hymen to thicken, and it becomes able to stretch without tearing, thus the lack of signs of past injury to the hymen in the pregnant adolescent girls.

Training programs, protocols and guidelines have been established to help medical providers from several disciplines learn to take care of victims of sexual assault, from infant to the elderly. In 2007, a group of colleagues and I published a set of guidelines for evaluating children and adolescents who may have been sexually abused[3]. The guidelines and the table listing an approach to the interpretation of physical and laboratory findings in suspected sexual abuse were developed using recommendations from the American Academy of Pediatrics, the Center for Disease Control, findings from research studies of abused and non-abused children, and a process of consensus development among a group of experts.

A small group of experts in Child Abuse Pediatrics began meeting again in 2010 to review new research and new recommendations for medical assessment and treatment of sexually abused children. The dialogue and consensus development process continued over several years, and the updated guidelines were published in 2015[4]. These guidelines are meant to provide medical providers with an update to the current state of research in the field of sexual abuse medical evaluation. One of the recommendations that came out of this consensus group is that examiners who see very few children each year for sexual abuse exams should carefully document their examination findings and have them reviewed by an expert clinician to make sure that their identification of injuries is accurate.

The ABC's of Sexual Assault is a great resource for everyone who is involved in the assessment, treatment, and support of victims of sexual assault. Medical and non-medical professionals who care for and interact with the legal system for child, adolescent and adult survivors will greatly benefit from the knowledge they attain after reading this excellent book.

Joyce A. Adams, MD
Clinical Professor of Pediatrics
University of California, Davis Medical Center
Specialist and Consultant in Child Abuse Pediatrics
jadams@ucsd.edu

References:

1.   Black MD, Basile KC, Breiding MJ, et al. The National Intimate Partner and Sexual Violence Survey (NISVS): 2010 Summary Report. Atlanta, GA: National Center for Injury Prevention and Control, Centers for Disease Control and Prevention; 2011

2.   Kellogg ND, Menard SW, Santos A. Genital anatomy in pregnant adolescents: "normal" doesn't mean "nothing happened". Pediatr 2004;223:e67-e69. http://www.pediatrics.org/cgi/content/full/113/1/e67

3.   Adams JA, Kaplan RA, Starling SP, et al: Guidelines for medical care for children who may have been sexually abused. J Pediatr Adolesc Gynecol 2007; 20:163-172

4.   Adams JA, Kellogg ND, Farst KJ, et al. Updated Guidelines for the Medical Assessment and Care of Children Who May Have Been Sexually Abused. Journal of Pediatric and Adolescent Gynecology (2015), doi: 10.1016/j.jpag.2015.01.007

Introduction

Scope and purpose of this book

This book is designed to be a simple guide for those who find themselves involved in the criminal justice system's processing of a sexual assault case. It is not designed to be an exhaustive resource or scholarly text. Instead, we want to provide a solid foundation of knowledge and understanding for every member of our sexual assault response teams (law enforcement officers, child protection case managers, prosecutors, victim advocates, medical and mental health professionals, forensic interviewers, etc.) as well as victims, family members, friends, those who have been accused, defense attorneys, judges and the media. This book is intended to be a desk-top guide or starting place.

Our goal is to present the truth as accurately and as fairly as we know how based upon our belief that the truth will convict those who are guilty of a crime and exonerate those who are not guilty. At the same time we recognize that no one, ourselves included, is personally or professionally capable of knowing and telling "the whole truth and nothing but the truth." Despite these limitations, we see the need for a reliable resource and have done our best to provide it. We encourage feedback from all of our readers so that we can edit and update this book, correcting any oversights or errors and incorporating new medical and legal advances as they develop.

About the cover

The broken letters used in the title reflect the physical and emotional condition of many patients when they first come to the Fort Wayne Sexual Assault Treatment Center and present for treatment. The broken letters can also represent members of a Sexual Assault Response Team who are overworked, underpaid, and conscientious but feeling burnt out, as well as a team whose effectiveness is undermined by misinformation and miscommunication, and a court system designed to protect the rights of defendants, often with little regard for their victims.

In contrast to this brokenness, the bamboo forest on the cover embodies our belief in the resilience of the human spirit and the need for each of us to be flexible enough to bend rather than break as we join together in the pursuit of justice in sexual assault cases. Bamboo is a giant but sturdy grass that grows quickly and regenerates fully. It symbolizes the healing and recovery we hope to cultivate through truth and understanding.

Information and Organization

Much of the information for this book comes from trainings, workshops and articles we have prepared together and presented professionally. We have organized the information into three sections: Anatomy, "Bunk" and the Courtroom. We have included a glossary at the end for quick reference as well as a list of recommended resources. Part 1: Anatomy is divided into sections on the examination and treatment of all patients, female anatomy, and male anatomy. Part 2: "Bunk" addresses common myths and misconceptions that often undermine the investigation and adjudication of sexual assault cases. We also look at the evolving definition of rape and the difference between criminal statutes that require force as an element and those that require only a lack of consent. Part 3: The Courtroom offers a very brief overview of criminal procedure for context and then considers the collection of forensic evidence and general guidance to assist attorneys and witnesses as they prepare for trial.

Experience and Expertise

Michelle Ditton has been an RN for 35 years with experience in the ER, NICU, telemetry, cardiac rehabilitation and pediatrics.

Michelle is a founder and the Chief Nursing Officer/CEO of the Fort Wayne Sexual Assault Treatment Center, a 501(c)(3) company that opened in 1996. The FWSATC was the first sexual assault center in Indiana and the first in the Midwest. Originally providing care to adults and adolescents ages 14 and older, in 2000 the Center began caring for children. The FWSATC is the recognized, credentialed medical provider for 16 counties in northeast Indiana. Its team of seven dedicated and competent forensic nurses serves approximately a million people and works with 56 law enforcement agencies.

Laurie Gray graduated from Indiana University Maurer School of Law in 1993, and her private practice included both civil and criminal trial work, plaintiffs' personal injury and insurance defense, workers compensation, medical malpractice, labor and employment, immigration, criminal defense, and Court-Appointed Guardian Ad Litem or Attorney for Parent in numerous CHINS (Child in Need of Services) cases. From 2000-2010, Laurie worked as an Allen County Deputy Prosecuting Attorney primarily in the areas of Felony Sex Crimes, the Drug Court Intervention Program, and Juvenile Sex Offenses. Laurie currently writes, speaks and consults through Socratic Parenting LLC and also works as an adjunct professor of criminal sciences at Indiana Tech and a bilingual child forensic interviewer at the Dr. Bill Lewis Center for Children.

We have been professional colleagues and friends since 2000 and have served together on the faculty at the National Symposium on Child Abuse in Huntsville, Alabama (2009 – 2014). For 15 years, we have worked together in the trenches, trained together, and sought better answers together. We are honored to share this information with you, and we encourage you to ask questions and find answers that work best for you.

The Fort Wayne Sexual Assault Treatment Center

In the fall of 1994, two emergency room nurses from Fort Wayne attended the 2nd annual International Association of

Forensic Nurses Conference in Virginia. It was there that they learned of the emerging specialty of Forensic Nursing. While many areas within the field were presented, it was the specialty practice of Sexual Assault Nurse Examiner (SANE) that was the most intriguing to them and the specific multi-disciplinary team concept of a Sexual Assault Response Team (SART) that they brought back to Indiana. In the months that followed, it became clear that many members of the community shared the common goal of providing the best medical forensic care to victims of sexual assault, and on January 29, 1996 the doors to the Fort Wayne Sexual Assault Treatment Center (FWSATC) were opened.

Not only was the Fort Wayne Sexual Assault Treatment Center the first of its kind in Indiana, it was one of only twenty in the United States. In its first year of operation, the FWSATC provided care to 123 adults and adolescents in Northeast Indiana who chose to report their crime of sexual assault. In June of 2000 services were expanded to provide the same comprehensive care to children. The FWSATC has been a pioneer in training and helping to establish other SART/SANE programs throughout the United States. Additionally, these nurses worked with different agencies at local, regional and state levels to provide the medical expertise necessary to implement best forensic practice in areas of legislation, guidelines, policies, evidence collection, and healthcare.

Today, there are over 700 sexual assault treatment centers in the United States, Canada, and Australia. Patients have increased three-fold, and the Fort Wayne Sexual Assault Treatment Center continues to be one of the leading healthcare providers and educators for treating victims of sexual assault. For more information on the Fort Wayne Sexual Assault Treatment Center, visit www.FWSATC.org.

Proceeds from this book will be shared equally for the benefit of the Fort Wayne Sexual Assault Treatment Center and Socratic Parenting LLC. For more information on Socratic Parenting LLC visit www.Socratic Parenting.com.

IMPORTANT NOTE:

The terms Sexual Assault Examiner (SAE), Sexual Assault Nurse Examiner (SANE), and Sexual Assault Forensic Examiner (SAFE) are sometimes used interchangeably. This book will focus on the SANE as the medical provider performing sexual assault examinations. **Any physician (MD or DO), nurse practitioner (NP) or physician's assistant (PA) who has the advanced training and clinical experience in sexual assault can perform all of the functions of a SANE and more according to their board certifications.** With regard to advanced training, the American Board of Pediatrics has a subspecialty certification in Child Abuse Pediatrics (CAP), and the International Association of Forensic Nurses (IAFN) has established guidelines for the specialized training of Sexual Assault Nurse Examiners (SANE).

A SANE is an RN with advanced training in sexual assault and should be certified as either a SANE-A (for adults and adolescents) or a SANE-P (for pediatrics), or both (as Michelle is). Because the author is a SANE, we will use the term SANE for simplicity and readability, but please be aware that many teams do have an SAE or SAFE that is an MD, DO, NP, or PA and who is able to provide differential diagnoses and additional treatments for injuries and infections beyond what a SANE can provide. Nevertheless, best practice requires all medical providers (SAEs and SAFEs) to follow the same standards of patient care when performing a sexual assault examination that the SANE follows. All SAEs, SAFEs and SANEs have the ability to testify as both fact witnesses and expert witnesses in cases of sexual assault.

While a physician or nurse practitioner is needed for a differential diagnosis, often the most qualified and experienced medical professionals performing sexual assault examinations are SANEs. As nurses, SANEs collaborate with the medical community. They submit their cases and photographs for regular peer review by those with appropriate credentials. In addition to their advanced training and certification, SANEs are required to participate in ongoing training relevant to sexual abuse and are better prepared to deal with this patient population than most hospital emergency departments, clinics, and family practitioners. SANEs respect both the medical and forensic needs of these patients, but their role is one: Patient care.

Both men and women work as SANEs. Because the author and all of the SANEs at the FWSATC are currently women, we will use feminine pronouns throughout the book when we refer to the SANE for consistency and clarity.

Part I

Anatomy

Chapter 1. The Sexual Assault Examination

The sexual assault examination has both medical and forensic components. The purpose of the sexual assault examination is to provide a timely, medical examination that addresses the patient's concerns, minimizes patient trauma, and promotes healing. The exam includes a standardized efficient procedure to collect the forensic evidence that can exonerate the innocent and hold criminals accountable. SANEs document facts and maintain records for both the legal and medical communities. At the same time, they provide the initial emotional, social, and crisis intervention their patients need.

Examples of the charts that a SANE at the FWSATC uses to document the sexual assault examination of an adult, adolescent or child are included in Appendix A. The forms demonstrate the clinical, therapeutic and forensic aspects of the examination for both adults and children. Clinically, the patient is assessed, diagnosed, and treated for the medical and mental health risks of sexual assault. Therapeutically, the patient receives information and support to address common myths (issues of virginity, whether or not they are now "damaged goods"), gender identity questions, and relationship problems. SANEs also provide appropriate recommendations and referrals for additional services. Forensically, SANEs document injury and collect evidence from the patient's body.

Emergency, Urgent and Non-Urgent Exams

Any time there is an acute complaint of bleeding or pain, suicidal ideations, or other safety concerns, the medical needs of the patient must come first. Emergency cases involving serious physical injury require the immediate care of qualified medical providers and may require that the patient be transported directly to the emergency department of a hospital. According to the Updated Guidelines for the Medical Assessment and Care of Children Who May Have Been Sexually Abused (2015), emergency cases may have both medical and forensic components. Assaults reported within 72 hours where DNA or other trace evidence may still be present are emergency cases. In those cases, a SANE may be called upon to perform the sexual assault examination at the hospital after the patient's medical condition is stabilized.

When no emergency exists, an urgent exam means that the sexual contact was recent and there may still be DNA, visible physical injury or other evidence on the patient's body. Adults and adolescents are only seen on an emergency or urgent basis. In Indiana, this means that the patient is reporting genital penetration in the last 96 hours, anal or oral penetration in the last 24 hours, or ongoing medical symptoms related to penetration if the 24 or 96 hours have already passed. Children may be seen on an emergency, urgent or non-urgent basis. An urgent case for children means genital penetration in the last two weeks. These time frames are typical, but may vary slightly from state to state, so it is important for the SANE to know the specific protocol in her state.

In emergency cases, especially where the sexual contact has occurred within the past 72 hours, best practice mandates that the sexual assault examination be performed as soon as possible, without delay. Every passing moment increases the risk that critical corroborating or exculpatory evidence will be lost. Patients become hungry, but consuming food or drink destroys the presence of DNA and trace evidence in an oral assault. Patients need to use the restroom, but normal toileting habits including wiping or changing a diaper, can remove DNA and trace evidence in cases of genital or anal assault. Washing the hands may also wash away a suspect's DNA from under the patient's fingernails. Any trace evidence on a patient's clothing may be lost as the patient moves from one place to another over time.

Each Sexual Assault Response Team must work together to establish its own reasonable guidelines for when a patient will be treated as a child for medical and interviewing purposes. The legal and medical worlds define "child," adolescent" and "adult" differently. In medicine, physical development controls while the laws in most states rely upon the person's chronological age.

Different medical experts have used different developmental scales and charts. The FWSATC uses Tanner Stages discussed in Chapter 2 for females and Chapter 3 for males. Generally speaking, a child is someone who is prepubescent or has not yet reached puberty. An adolescent is someone who has undergone puberty but not yet reached full maturity. An adult has reached full growth or maturity. Pediatrics is the branch of medicine that specializes in infants and children, but a pediatrician's expertise extends to include adolescents and young adults, too.

State laws vary as to when exactly a child becomes an adolescent or juvenile, when a teenager is able to engage in consensual sexual acts, and when a minor reaches the age of majority. In some states 16 and 17-year olds are old enough to consent to sexual activity with an adult of any age, but in other states they are not. Depending on state definitions, a sexual assault may be categorized as child molesting when the victim is a child or statutory rape when the victim is a teenager, but still a minor, and unable to give legal consent. We address the age of consent in more detail in Chapter 6.

Overview of the Sexual Assault Exam

Each sexual assault examination includes an introduction, health history, head-to-toe examination, genital examination, medical diagnosis, treatment and discharge instruction, and follow-up examination as needed. Throughout the examination, forensic evidence is collected based upon the history given and sexual assault training. We will deal in more detail with the female genital examination in Chapter 2, the male genital examination in Chapter 3, and with the collection of forensic evidence in Chapter 8. In this first chapter we will focus on the history, head-to-toe examination, diagnosis, treatment and discharge, as well as the need for follow-up examinations.

When first addressing the patient, the SANE introduces herself as a nurse. If the patient is a child, the SANE explains that she wants to make sure that the child is okay. If the child's case requires an emergency exam (assault within the past 72 hours), the

SANE will explain to the child and family that in most cases there are no injuries to the child's genitals. (This will be explained in more detail in Chapter 8, with a specific example in the Jent case). In the few cases where there are genital injuries, these injuries typically heal very quickly and without residual evidence of injury. If the child's case is urgent or non-urgent (assault outside the 72-hour window), the SANE will explain to the child and the family that the examination could be normal, depending on the history and timing of the last event. The nurse also explains the equipment she'll be using and what to expect during the examination. At the end of the introduction, the SANE takes a photo of the face of the patient for identification.

The patient's health history includes the past medical history, current medications, allergies, and recent injuries (within 60 days). The SANE then addresses current symptoms, especially any complaints of pain or bleeding and how it felt to urinate. Complaints are recorded using the patient's exact words in quotation marks. The SANE also records the patient's height, weight and vital signs. Regardless of whether the patient is an adult, adolescent or child, the history of the current complaint comes from the patient and is charted verbatim.

The SANE will never force an examination. SANEs reassure patients, especially children, that they are okay, that they are not damaged, and that this is not their fault. When done correctly, the sexual assault examination does not cause the child physical pain, nor should it ever cause additional trauma. Instead, the examination actually helps to reduce trauma and promote healing. Children often present feeling afraid and ashamed. After talking with the nurse, having their whole body checked, and learning that their bodies are okay and their feelings are normal, children leave feeling much better than they did before the sexual assault examination.

All of the research confirms the benefits of a pediatric sexual assault examination. Children who do not receive a competent medical/forensic examination to address their concerns following a sexual assault are almost certain to have poor long-term health consequences as adults. Sexual assault is not like a cold; people don't just "get over it." It's a crime—a physical, mental, emotional, and spiritual violation of their whole person. The sooner they have someone to address their physical needs and emotional concerns, the sooner the healing can begin.

Only a qualified medical provider can actually look at a child's whole body, including his genitals and anus, and tell him that he is, or will be, okay. A SANE can assure children that no one will ever be able to look at them and tell that they were sexually assaulted. Counselors, child protection professionals, law enforcement, victim advocates—no one else can ever ask a child to disrobe and reassure her that she really is okay. Most emergency, family and pediatric physicians are trained only to look for and treat significant physical trauma. SANEs are trained to assess and treat both the medical and psychological needs of this patient population.

The patient undresses for the head-to-toe examination so that the SANE may look for physical injuries or medical conditions on every part of the body. Any injuries observed are documented on the full-body diagrams as seen below in Illustration 1a. Multiple injuries to the head, hands, feet, ears, or inside the mouth are documented using diagrams like those in Illustrations 1b and 1c below.

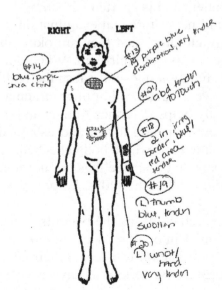

Illustration 1a

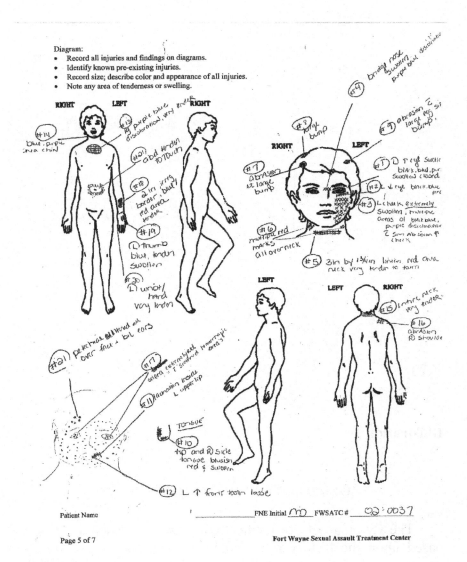

Diagram:
- Record all injuries and findings on diagrams.
- Identify known pre-existing injuries.
- Record size; describe color and appearance of all injuries.
- Note any area of tenderness or swelling.

Patient Name _____   FNE Initial ___   FWSATC # _____ 92 : 0037

Page 5 of 7   Fort Wayne Sexual Assault Treatment Center

Illustration 1b

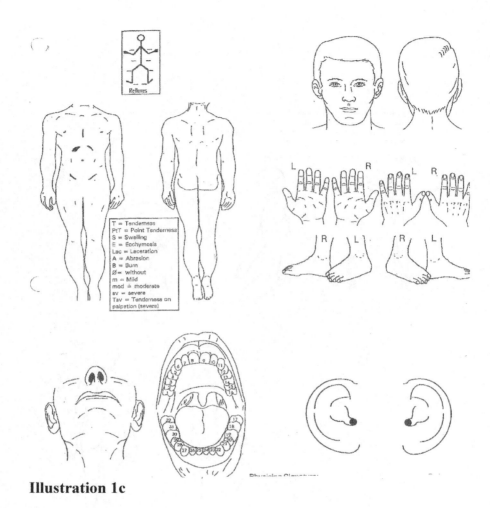

Illustration 1c

Diagnosis, Treatment and Discharge

The vast majority of medical diagnoses (as much as 90%) is based upon the history provided by the patient. A patient who presents with a history of migraines and complaint of a headache will very likely be diagnosed with and treated for a migraine based on the patient history alone. There are no tests to run to confirm that the pain, nausea, etc. are caused by a migraine. But first the medical provider considers the chronological order of events that has led the patient to seek medical attention. Depending upon the history, specific tests may be ordered to rule out other possible causes of the current complaint. We approach sexual assault as we would any other medical condition: We take the history and examine the patient before making a diagnosis and recommending a course of treatment. We take and record a complete medical history (including psychotropic medications, sexually transmitted infections and prior assaults) regardless of any potential legal consequences. The legal ramifications will be handled by the court. The medical record must be complete and accurate.

As with all medical examinations, the purpose of the sexual assault examination is the diagnosis and treatment of the patient's condition. When the history is sexual assault, the provider must examine the patient for any medical and/or psychological residual effects of the sexual contact. Residual effects can include genital trauma, anal trauma, sexually transmitted infections (STI's), and the presence of foreign evidence.

What most people who watch "CSI" and other crime drama on television fail to realize is that 90-95% of patients will have normal exams. As we will discuss in great detail in the next chapter on the female anatomy and in Chapter 8 on collecting evidence, a "normal" exam can be consistent with a history of sexual assault, even penetration. Likewise, an examination that reveals genital or anal trauma may be indicative of sexual contact, but does not necessarily indicate sexual assault when the patient is able to consent and gives a history of having consented to the contact that resulted in the injury. There are no foregone conclusions, and the examination itself can never be considered in isolation as the sole proof that a sexual assault did or did not occur.

As noted in the introduction, physicians, nurse practitioners and physician assistants are able to provide more differential diagnoses related to specific medical conditions than SANEs are, but nurses can and do diagnose their patients, too. Suppose a man presents at the emergency department with a history of having fallen off of a ladder and complains of arm pain. He is not immediately attended to by the physician on duty. Instead, he is triaged and cared for by a registered nurse whose job it is to take a history, form a nursing diagnosis and provide immediate treatment. A nurse can examine the arm, assess the swelling, pain, bruising, sensation and movement and treat these symptoms by elevating, positioning and icing the arm and also dispensing prescription medication based upon her nursing diagnosis and the physician's standing order. Care is taken to ensure that the patient does not go into shock. If the bone has obvious deformity, such as the bone protruding through the skin, she can make a general nursing assessment regarding the deformity. She must also monitor the color in the hand and fingers to ensure that there is adequate circulation and movement of the arm, hand and fingers. It will be up to the physician, NP or PA to review x-rays and provide the differential diagnosis regarding the exact location and type of fracture and determine whether the best course of treatment is to set the broken arm or whether surgery is required.

Just like a nurse in the emergency department, a SANE diagnoses and treats patients who present with a history of sexual assault. The most common nursing diagnoses following a sexual assault examination are acute pain, risk of infection and risk of Post-Trauma Syndrome. NANDA International (formerly the North American Nursing Diagnosis Association) lists dozens of nursing diagnoses that can and do pertain to sexual assault patients. An expanded list of Nursing Diagnoses defined by NANDA International for 2015-2017 that frequently apply to sexual assault patients is included as Appendix B.

Sexually transmitted infections (STIs) used to be called sexually transmitted diseases (STDs), but that term has fallen out of use by the medical profession. This topic is far too complex to address fully in this book. Some STIs like gonorrhea, syphilis, chlamydia and trichomonas can be clear indicators of sexual abuse in children once other possibilities of acquiring the infection are ruled out. HIV is indicative of sexual contact if transmission by blood transfusion has been ruled out. Other infections such as herpes and condyloma accuminata are suspicious and should probably be reported if other causes have been ruled out. Medical providers must check with their own state health department for the list of STIs they are required to report. STIs are a strong reason to suspect sexual abuse in children when other causes have been ruled out. Illustration 1d is the chart prepared by the Center for Disease Control (CDC) on what to report.

Implications of Commonly Encountered STIs for Diagnosis and Reporting of Suspected or Diagnosed Sexual Abuse of Children

STI Confirmed	Sexual Abuse	Suggested Action
Gonorrhea[1]	Diagnostic	Report
Syphilis[1]	Diagnostic	Report
HIV	Diagnostic	Report
Chlamydia[1]	Diagnostic	Report
Trichomonas	Highly suspicious	Report
Condyloma accuminata[1]	Suspicious	Report
Herpes[2]	Suspicious	Report
Bacterial vaginosis	Inconclusive	Medical Follow-up

[1] If not perinatally acquired and rare nonsexual vertical transmission is excluded

[2] Unless there is a clear history of autoinoculation

AAP Red Book, 2006

CDC STD Guidelines, 2010, page 93

Illustration 1d

Incubation periods for STIs vary. Screening for an STI immediately after an acute, one-time assault is rarely helpful and likely to miss an infection related to the sexual contact. STIs from prior contact may or may not be present. Chlamydia is a very common STI, often with no symptoms. The incubation period for chlamydia is a minimum of 7 days while it takes syphilis 10-90 days to develop. The incubation period for gonorrhea is 2-7 days. After that a patient is likely to exhibit some symptoms such as discharge (genital, anal and oral mucosa), painful urination, lesions, redness, and pain. Even when symptoms are apparent, however, a test must be done to confirm the infection.

STI testing is indicated for some sexual assault patients, but not for all. The assessment must be made on an individual basis and can depend on the age of the patient, the history of the assault, the timing of the examination, suspect characteristics including whether the suspect is known to have an STI or to be at a high risk for an STI, whether other household members have an STI, and evidence of genital, oral or anal penetration or ejaculation. Patients may also request the testing. A patient who may have been exposed to HIV within the past 72 hours should receive preventative medications immediately (the sooner the better). Current protocol is to give all adults and adolescents who are at risk for an STI after sexual assault antibiotics as preventative treatment rather than test for STIs. Preventative medications include Rocephin or Zithromax for gonorrhea and Doxycycline or Zithromax for chlamydia.

The protocol for children is different. Overprescribing antibiotics in children increases the development of antibiotic-resistant bacteria or "superbugs." Children may also be more susceptible to side effects such as stomach upset, diarrhea, and allergic reactions. In children, the best practice is to wait until a specific STI has been identified and treat that STI. Some methods of STI identification may be sufficient for treatment purposes, but not admissible in court as conclusive evidence of the STI. Preventative treatment for HIV must be given within 72 hours of the sexual assault, and the sooner the better. For HIV prevention only, there is a trend toward providing treatment in all cases of sexual assault where there is a history of penetration by an unknown suspect that occurred within the prior 72 hours. All patients may also receive a booster dose of Tetanus and Diphtheria Toxoid if it has been more than five years since their last booster dose.

Finally, best practice requires that hormonal therapy (or the morning after pill) be offered as an option to any patient who has had at least one menstrual cycle and is not post-menopausal (no menses for one year). There are various medications available for this hormonal therapy option with different mechanisms of actions depending on which medication is administered. All of these hormonal therapies act to PREVENT pregnancy. Different hormones work differently, but NONE of these medications induce abortion from a medical standpoint. They may prevent an egg from being released, or interfere with fertilization of the egg by the sperm, or inhibit implantation of a fertilized egg in the uterus. These are methods of contraception, not abortion.

The National Protocol for Sexual Assault Medical Forensic Examinations, the International Association of Forensic Nurses (IAFN), the American College of Emergency Physicians (ACEP) and the American Academy of Pediatrics (AAP) all require that hormonal therapy be offered as an OPTION in order to meet the minimum standard of care. It is always up to the patient whether or not she accepts or declines the offer of hormonal treatment. Moreover, she should feel free to ask for additional information about how the specific hormonal therapies being offered work before making her decision.

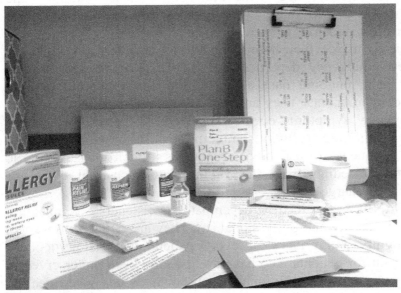

Illustration 1e

Along with the administration of medications and treatment, SANEs must provide some instruction for the patient and family regarding the treatment and discharge plan and coordinate referrals in a way that optimizes compliance and follow-up care. A photograph of the various treatment options is included as Illustration 1e.

Please note that for those medications that require a prescription, only physicians and nurse practitioners are licensed by the Drug Enforcement Agency (DEA) to prescribe controlled substances. Physician's assistants and registered nurses are not licensed to prescribe controlled substances, but may dispense them under the authority of a doctor or nurse practitioner. The FWSATC works with two physicians who have provided standing orders on which medications should be prescribed based on the SANE's examination and diagnosis and who review the medications actually provided to individual patients.

As outlined on the Discharge Instructions in Appendix A, care and treatment of the patient may include assessment of physical injuries, the collection of forensic samples and specimens, a urine test for pregnancy, the administration of medication, and follow-up recommendations. Patients are always instructed to see their family doctor immediately or go to the nearest emergency department if they experience severe pain, chest pain, ongoing nausea or vomiting or any other unusual medical complaints. They are also told to call their family doctor if any new symptoms occur such as fever, genital/rectal pain, sores or discharge, urinary symptoms (painful urination, blood in urine, frequency of urination) or changes in their menstrual cycle (unusual bleeding from the vagina, late menstrual cycle, or vaginal discharge).

SANEs are trained to be empathetic listeners and maintain their objectivity and professionalism. They are required to respect the dignity and privacy of every patient. This is particularly important for patients who have traditionally been underserved in a way that creates additional psychosocial issues when dealing with sexual violence. Some examples of patient populations that have been overlooked and underserved in the past include men, prison inmates, military personnel, patients with disabilities or mental health issues, adolescents, LGBT/Queer patients, and patients with cultural or language differences. SANEs have the foundational knowledge to assess and treat these sexual assault patients and collaborate with them to find the community resources they need.

When appropriate, the SANE will ask the patient to return for a follow-up examination. During the follow-up exam, the SANE can document the healing of any injuries, confirm that discoloration was due to bruising or other injury rather than a normal variant, check the patient's medical status, reassure the patient and make any needed referrals for additional medical, psychological or legal services. A Follow-Up Medical Forensic Examination Chart is included in Appendix A as item A-5.

Examination Results

Regardless of who performs the sexual assault examination, no medical provider can examine a patient to determine if the patient is still a virgin or if semen is present. We will discuss these myths and misconceptions in more detail in Chapters 2, 4 and 8. A sexual assault examination can reveal a normal exam, conditions mistaken for abuse, injuries caused by trauma, and other medical conditions. Forensic evidence can be collected and submitted for DNA analysis, but it is impossible for the person collecting the evidence to know whether DNA is even present, let alone whose DNA it might be. A sexual assault examination CANNOT prove that the patient was or was not sexually assaulted, that the hymen is "missing" or "intact," who caused the injury, what caused the injury, or whether or not the contact was consensual (if the patient is able to consent).

These common myths and misperceptions are very real and the legal and medical ramifications most disturbing. In 2009, the Supreme Court of Appeals of West Virginia upheld a trial court's order that a 15-year-old girl undergo a sexual assault examination for the sole purpose of determining whether or not the girl's hymen had be penetrated by one defendant's penis after the other defendant had admitted to digitally penetrating the girl. *State ex rel. J.W. v. Knight*, 223 S.E.2d 617 (W. Va. 2009). Both defendants were the girl's older brothers and the allegations were that they began sexually assaulting her when she was nine years old. Both the trial court and the appellate court mistakenly believed that a medical expert could not only look at a hymen to see if it had been penetrated, but also determine whether or not a hymen that had admittedly been penetrated by one brother's finger had also been penetrated by the other brother's penis.

The trial court granted and the appellate court upheld the discovery request of the second brother based on the completely false belief that the examination of the girl's genitalia might provide exculpatory evidence not otherwise available to the defendant. No one in the West Virginia medical or legal community provided the presiding judges with accurate medical information about the female sex organ or what a sexual assault examination can and cannot reveal. It is time for our medical and legal communities to join together, educate ourselves, and dispel the myths that have caused us to re-victimize survivors of sexual assault. This book represents our best effort toward that end.

Chapter 2. Female Anatomy

We've all heard it: Boys have penises and girls have vaginas. Most people have seen a penis, but hardly anyone ever actually sees a vagina. Although often used as a vague reference to anything and everything in the area of the female genitalia, the vagina is really only the birth canal. It is an internal organ. In this chapter, we will look specifically at the female anatomy and identify the parts that are most pertinent in sexual assault cases.

In this book, we often refer to the female genitals as the female sex organ (FSO). This is a legal term, not a medical term. Indiana law, and the law in many states, does not require that the vagina be penetrated. Instead, the slightest degree of penetration of the FSO by the male sex organ (MSO) is included in the definition of sexual intercourse and sufficient to sustain a sexual assault conviction. When it comes to the female anatomy, the prepositions "on" and "in" can be the difference between the lowest level felony and the highest level felony. A penis, finger or object does NOT need to be "in" the vagina to be "in" the FSO.

The medical term for the visible parts of the FSO is vulva. Think of the vulva as a chamber protected by double doors that open outward. Those double doors are the labia majora. If the doors are closed and only the outside of the doors are touched, then this is "on" the FSO. Anything inside those doors is "in" the FSO. Illustration 2a shows what lies beyond the doors and "in" the FSO. Inside the FSO are two holes, the urethra where urine passes and the vaginal opening leading to the vagina or birth canal. The anus, where stool passes, is not part of the FSO. The area between the FSO and the anus is called the perineum. Male anatomy also includes the perineum between the scrotum and the anus. The sexual assault examination of the anus is exactly the same for males and females and will be covered in detail in the next chapter.

There are multiple ways to visualize the FSO using various positions and techniques. One common position is known as supine, which simply means that the patient is lying on the examination table face up, with her back on the table.

Gynecological examinations of women are normally performed in the lithotomy position (patient supine, scooted down to the edge of the examination table and with her feet raised above her hips

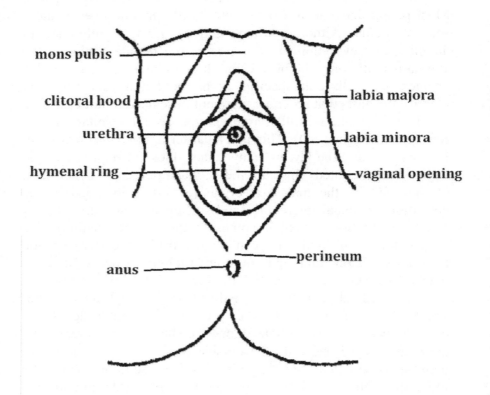

mons pubis

clitoral hood

urethra

hymenal ring

labia majora

labia minora

vaginal opening

anus

perineum

Illustration 2a

and usually held in place by stirrups). For small children, the supine frog-leg position is used where the child lies on her back, pulls her knees up to her chest, and puts the soles of her feet together to spread her legs. SANE's typically use multiple positions, including the prone knee-chest position where the patient is face down and rests on the knees and upper part of the chest. This allows for an expanded alternate view of the FSO and also of the anus.

A clear plastic speculum like the one in the middle of Illustration 8a (p. 83) is inserted into the vagina in adolescents and adults to widen the opening and visualize the vagina and cervix for injuries. On p. 6 of the Adult Medical Forensic Examination Chart for a female, there is a diagram of the vagina and cervix viewed through a traditional metal speculum with part of the speculum handle shown at the bottom. The right side of the diagram depicts the mechanism used to hold the speculum blades open. A speculum is never used on a prepubescent child. There are other techniques that aid in the visualization of the FSO of a child. The first technique is known as "separation," where the SANE separates the labia majora and labia minora with gloved fingers to assess for injury and complaints of pain or tenderness. Even better visualization can be achieved using traction, where the SANE (again with gloved fingers), holds the labia majora and minora at different angles. Another technique, "floating the hymen" with saline or water, uses saline or water to unstick and separate the folds of the hymen for better visualization. A Foley catheter can also be used to visualize the hymen of an adult or adolescent. This is a flexible plastic tube that has a balloon on the tip. When the SANE inflates the balloon, she can see the entire hymenal ring without causing pain to the patient.

All visible injuries are recorded on the SANE's chart and marked on the diagram of the FSO. Frequently the location of injuries on and in the FSO is referenced like the face of a clock, with 12:00 at the very top, 6:00 at the very bottom, 3:00 on the right (patient's left) and 9:00 on the left (patient's right). An abrasion on the lower right portion of the labia minora might be described as an abrasion on the labia minora at 4:00. A bruise on the upper left (patient's right) part of the hymen might be described as a bruised hymen at 11:00.

The Truth about the Hymen

The hymen is without a doubt the most misunderstood little membrane in the history of the human race. The word itself comes from the Greek wedding god (Hymen) and the songs sung to join the couple together in matrimony (hymenaios).   Over the centuries, it became a false symbol of virginity. In a patriarchal society without the science of DNA, men who wanted to preserve their bloodline needed to marry a virgin and ensure that she never had the opportunity to engage in sexual intercourse with any other man. When it came to marriage, a woman's virginity was her most precious asset, and people began to believe that a woman should bleed when a marriage is consummated as proof of her virginity. The idea that the hymen sealed a woman's vaginal opening until she engaged in sexual intercourse for the first time may be very comforting to men who want to marry a virgin or women who want proof of their virginity, but they are still false ideas based upon mistaken beliefs.

Such beliefs are not based on any medical evidence. As we will explain in this section, they simply are not true. Unfortunately, there are still many physicians and nurses who do not specialize in sexual assault and have never been taught the basics of female anatomy. Without proper training and education, even some of our most trusted physicians are more likely to base their examinations and findings on these hymenal myths than on the real, medical facts about the hymen. We address many of these myths as "bunk" in Chapter 4. In this chapter, we want to focus on the facts.

FACT: The hymen is a stretchy membrane like a collar around the entrance to the vagina (birth canal). Appendix C contains an extensive list of peer-reviewed articles that support our assertions about the female anatomy and the sexual assault medical examination.

When our SANEs testify in court, we have them bring a hair scrunchy with them to use as a teaching tool to educate the jury (and the lawyers). They wear it around their wrists and pull it off when they talk about the hymen. They demonstrate for the jury how the hymen "scrunches up" and might look like a membrane that completely covers the vaginal opening. But it does not act as a barrier to the vagina. Sometimes we even insert a speculum into the hair scrunchy and open it up to demonstrate how far a hymen can stretch without causing any injury at all. As a girl approaches puberty, her body produces estrogen, and that estrogen makes the hymenal membrane elastic enough for a tampon, penis or even a baby to pass through without causing injury. Of course, sometimes there is injury based upon force, size or insufficient lubrication, but that injury is no more likely to happen on the first penetration of the estrogenized hymen than it is on any subsequent penetration.

Many otherwise competent physicians have examined the genitalia of a child and concluded that the hymen is "missing" or "intact." There are no peer-reviewed cases of a girl being born without a hymen. A child with some male parts and some female parts is considered androgynous (sex undetermined) or a hermaphrodite (both male and female). There is no credible report of any female child ever being born without a hymen. There are still many reports, however, where an untrained medical provider does not recognize the hymen and charts that it is "missing." Likewise, there are still physicians who visualize the "scrunched up" hymen and chart that it is "intact." In fact, in very rare cases the hymen may be imperforate. This requires surgery to allow the passage of menstrual blood and prevent infection. There are also physicians who offer a surgical procedure to "repair the hymen" or "restore virginity." There is absolutely no benefit to sewing up a woman's hymen and many potential medical complications. Surgeries with no medical benefits that alter the female genitalia for cultural reasons are discussed in more detail in the section on female genital mutilation later in this chapter.

Virginity is not a physical state or medical condition. It is a social construct based upon religious and cultural values with no universally accepted definition. Some people define a virgin as anyone who has never engaged in heterosexual intercourse. Others say that the term virgin only applies to females. Many now describe a virgin as someone who has never engaged in an intimate relationship that included oral, anal or vaginal sex. We have seen cases where a girl or woman was anally raped and the family was relieved that she is still a "virgin." The inference is that her value as a person would somehow be diminished if she engaged in sexual intercourse before marriage, regardless of whether the intercourse was forced or by consent. There are others who believe that a person's virginity belongs to that individual and can only be freely given. A person who is sexually molested as a child or sexually assaulted as an adolescent or adult could still be a "virgin" under this definition. Whatever our definition of "virgin" is, it is important that we all recognize it as a social, religious or cultural belief and realize that some people will agree with us, some will not, and that there is no legal or medical definition that can determine once and for all who is correct.

A properly trained SANE knows that normal female anatomy does not all look alike. A normal hymen may be annular, crescentic or fimbriated. An annular hymen extends completely around the circumference of the vaginal opening like a collar or ring. A crescentic hymen is shaped like a crescent moon. A fimbriated hymen has many projections along the edge which give it a ruffled appearance. Different women also have different pigmentation, particularly those of differing ethnicity. Darker pigmentation on any part of the FSO is completely normal, but it is sometimes mistaken for bruising or injury. If there is any doubt whether the darker area is normal or an injury, the patient should be asked to return for a follow-up examination after any injury has had time to heal to determine if it was an injury or normal for this patient.

The normal hymen also undergoes significant hormonal changes from birth through puberty and after menopause. Estrogen is the female hormone that causes the hymen to become thick and elastic. When a baby is first born, she may still have enough of her mother's residual estrogen present to keep the hymen elastic for months or even years. That estrogen diminishes, though, so from as early as three months to as late as three years until the onset of puberty, the young girl's hymen becomes very thin and vascular in appearance and is painful to touch. Attempting to penetrate an unestrogenized hymen with a tampon, finger or penis can cause significant pain and injury to the hymen. As the child's body matures, she begins to produce her own estrogen and the hymen becomes pale, thick and elastic (like a scrunchy). By the time a girl begins to menstruate, a tampon, finger, or penis can pass through the hymen without causing any injury or pain. Anything that is inserted at an awkward angle, with significant force or without lubrication can still cause injury, but such injury is not a foregone conclusion.

Tanner Stages

The sequence of sexual maturation is predictable, and it is helpful to describe the sequence of changes. A British pediatrician by the name of James Tanner created a scale of sexual development known as the Tanner scale or Tanner stages to identify whether a patient should be physically treated as a child, adolescent or adult. The five Tanner stages of development for a female are primarily marked by breast and pubic hair distribution.

Stage 1: Prepubertal with no breast development or pubic hair.
Stage 2: Breasts bud, and areola enlarges; sparse growth of long, slightly pigmented hair (straight or curled) along the labia.
Stage 3: Further enlargement of breast and areola; darker, coarser and more curled hair spreading sparsely over the mons pubis.
Stage 4: Areola and papilla form a secondary mound above the level of the breast; adult pubic hair covering small area of the mons pubis.
Stage 5: Mature stage, areola recesses and only papilla projects; adult pubic hair in full quantity with horizontal (feminine) distribution.

A developing child may be in one Tanner stage according to her breasts and another according to pubic hair distribution. Regardless of the Tanner Stage a patient is in, a speculum should never be used as part of the sexual assault examination until after the girl reports the onset of menses. SANEs must also be cognizant that the body loses estrogen with menopause and be certain that they use adequate lubrication and care if a speculum exam is needed on a post-menopausal woman.

Female Genital Mutilation (FGM)

While male circumcision is an accepted practice in the United States, female circumcision is an extremely harmful form of genital mutilation that offers absolutely no medical benefit and creates a multitude of life-threatening medical consequences.18 U.S. Code § 116 prohibits the genital mutilation of any female less than 18 years of age in the United States. As of January 2015, 23 states also have statutes making FGM a crime. Still, it is practiced in other parts of the world such as Africa, the Middle East and Asia, and American girls may be subjected to FGM when they are on vacation in their parents' countries of origin or by circumcisers brought into the United States. The American author Alice Walker first raised public awareness on this issue through her novel *Possessing the Secret of Joy* in 1992. A year later she collaborated with Pratibha Parmar to investigate and document the practice in their nonfiction book and documentary film *Warrior Marks*.

Unlike male circumcision which removes only the foreskin, FGM removes part or all of the female genitalia. The World Health Organization classifies FGM into four major types: Clitoridectomy (partial or total removal of the clitoris), Excision (partial or total removal of the clitoris and the labia minora), Infibulation (the most extreme form, this can include removing all external genitalia and stitching together the two sides of the labia majora), and Other (all other harmful procedures that serve no medical purpose, including pricking, piercing, incising, scraping and cauterizing the genital area). FGM has no health benefits and the health consequences can be dire. Immediate complications include severe pain (traditionally the ritual is performed without anesthetic), shock, infection, tetanus, uncontrolled bleeding, and urine retention. Long-term consequences include recurrent bladder and urinary tract infections, cysts, infertility, an increased risk of childbirth complications and newborn deaths, and the need for later surgeries. In the case of infibulation, the "seal" created must be cut open later to allow for sexual intercourse and childbirth.

FGM is recognized internationally as an extreme form of discrimination against women that violates basic human rights to health, security and physical integrity, the right to be free from torture, and even the right to life because FGM carries a high risk of death. In 1996, the United States granted 17-year-old Fauziya Kasinga asylum after she escaped from Togo to avoid FGM and forced marriage. *See Matter of Kasinga*, 21 I. & N. 357 (BIA 1996). In December 2012, the United Nations General Assembly adopted a resolution on the elimination of FGM. Recently, the U.S. government has undertaken a nationwide study on FGM to determine how many women and girls are living with the consequences of FGM or are at risk of FGM in the U.S., and to provide guidance to all U.S. Attorneys on investigating and prosecuting cases of FGM. In October 2014, the U.S. Departments of Health and Human Services, Education, Justice, Immigration, and several others, hosted a consultation with civil society on how to best address FGM in the U.S. For more information on the elimination of FGM, visit http://www.equalitynow.org/resources.

More than 125 million females in the world today have been subjected to the ritual mutilation of their genitals, and SANEs must be prepared to recognize, assess and treat these women and children. Since the FWSATC first opened its doors in 1996, only two patients have presented with a history of FGM. In both cases the wounds from the circumcision had healed, but it was important to chart very carefully what parts of the FSO were present and what parts were altered or missing. The need for sensitivity in each case was paramount and complicated by cultural and language barriers. There were also two patients who were about to be subjected to FGM, but with appropriate education and actions by the treating SANEs, those circumcisions were prevented. More frequently seen is the voluntary piercing of the clitoral hood and/or labia in adult women. Such piercings can serve as a reservoir for suspect DNA. SANEs must take extra care in swabbing around such piercings and sometimes collect them as forensic evidence.

Chapter 3. Male Anatomy

In contrast to female anatomy, all medical providers are trained to correctly and consistently identify the basic male anatomy that they observe during a sexual assault examination. Likewise, most lay persons and many children can consistently identify the penis, testicles and scrotum. We have identified the basic parts of the male anatomy for you in Illustration 3a. Just as it is normal for a very young boy to get an erection during a diaper change or bath, it is quite normal for a male of any age to get an erection during the sexual assault examination. It is important to assure the patient even prior to the exam that this is normal.

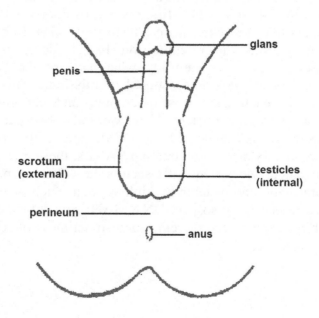

Illustration 3a

Tanner Stages

The Tanner scale created by the British pediatrician discussed in the last chapter is also used to mark a boy's physical development through adolescence into adulthood. The Tanner stages for a male are marked by genital and pubic hair distribution.

Stage 1: Prepubertal with no pubic hair.
Stage 2: Scrotum and testes enlarge, scrotum skin reddens and changes in texture; sparse growth of long, slightly pigmented hair (straight or curled) at the base of the penis.
Stage 3: Penis lengthens, further growth of testes; more curled hair spreading sparsely over the mons pubis or pubic mound.
Stage 4: Penis grows in breadth, glans develops, testes and scrotum grow larger, scrotum skin darkens; adult pubic hair covering small area of the mons pubis.
Stage 5: Adult genitalia; adult pubic hair in full quantity with spread to medial surface of thighs.

Circumcision

Circumcision (which literally means "cutting around") involves removing some or all of the foreskin from around the tip of the penis. Look at the diagrams of the male sex organ on page 6 of 7 in Appendix A-1 (p. 113). The penis in the drawing with the legs spread appears to be circumcised. The penises in the left and right side-view drawings below that look more like an uncircumcised penis. While it is never correct to say that a hymen is intact, it is correct to describe the foreskin as intact on an uncircumcised penis.

Circumcision is common in the United States and may be a matter of religion, family tradition, personal hygiene or preventive health care. The American Academy of Pediatrics does not recommend routine circumcision for all newborn boys, but it does say that the medical benefits of circumcision outweigh the medical risks. For additional information on the benefits and risks associated with circumcision, as well as drawings comparing the appearance of a circumcised penis and uncircumcised penis, visit www.MayoClinic.org and do a website search for "circumcision."

Whether or not the penis is circumcised has little impact on the sexual assault examination. If the foreskin has separated from the glans, the SANE should gently pull it back to check for injury and trace evidence and to swab for DNA. The foreskin will usually slide back easily on an adult. If it does not, however, a SANE should never force back the foreskin, especially not on a young boy. In the meantime, the appearance of a cheesy looking substance called smegma (Greek for "soap") under the foreskin is normal residue from cells being shed as the foreskin separates from the glans. Until the foreskin has fully separated from the glans, attempting to retract it may cause pain, bleeding and injury.

Anal Anatomy

There is no structural or functional difference between the male anus and the female anus. All information provided in this section applies equally to females. Part of the normal function of the anus is to open or dilate to allow the passage of stool without damaging tissue. We've all passed stools and even children can pass stools large enough to clog a toilet. For this reason, it is extremely rare to detect anal injuries in cases of anal penetration. Only about 1% of cases will result in injury and these are often due to the size or angle of the penetrating object, the presence of significant force, and/or the lack of lubrication.

In cases where there are anal or superficial injuries, most will heal rapidly and completely. When we pass a large stool, there may be a small amount of blood on the toilet paper, but any pain, bleeding or discomfort passes very quickly. There is also no distinguishing difference between an "exit wound" and an "entrance wound." In other words, passing a large, dry stool out can cause the same type of injury as forcing a penis or object of similar size and shape in. A normal exam certainly does not mean that there was no sexual assault, and anal injuries do not necessarily mean that a sexual assault occurred. The medical history is critical in these diagnoses and in determining whether observations during the examination are consistent with the history provided by the patient.

Two Anal Assault Cases

Michelle vividly recalls a case several years ago when a very well-meaning, but insufficiently trained, pediatrician looked at an 8-year-old boy's anus and mistook the median raphe where the two halves of the perineum meet for anal scarring and sexual abuse. The boy gave no history of sexual assault, and the family was thrown into a quagmire of false and fearful allegations. Child protection stepped in and removed the child from the home altogether at precisely the time he most needed his parental and family support. It took another examination by an experienced Sexual Assault Examiner and an order from a judge to return the boy home where he belonged. Still, the trauma to the child and the family was immeasurable.

Michelle recalls another 10-year-old boy who had been groomed and sexually abused by an uncle. He arrived at the FWSATC feeling embarrassed, ashamed, conflicted and confused. He stated that he did not wish to be examined, and as noted in Chapter 1, a SANE will never force an examination. Instead, Michelle talked to the boy. He had expressed an interest in trucks in the waiting room, so Michelle asked him how he would choose the very best truck. After some discussion, he admitted that he really would want to see the truck before he could decide if it was the best one. Michelle explained that she believed he was okay, but that she really couldn't tell him that for sure without examining him. He decided to have the examination and in the process disclosed that his father had suggested he should have fought his uncle off and that maybe he was a "homo." The boy was terrified because his uncle's abuse had aroused him sexually and the abuse felt good. Michelle was able to reassure him that he was physically okay and that no one would ever be able to look at him in the shower or in the locker room and know what his uncle had done. She also assured him that sex does feel good, and that it was natural for him to respond to sexual stimulation. He felt conflicted because he still cared for his uncle and didn't want him to go to prison.

Michelle assured the boy that it was okay to care about his family and friends even when they do something very bad, and that whatever happened to his uncle was because of the choices his uncle made, not because of what the young boy had or hadn't done. Finally, Michelle assured him that when he was older, he would know who he was attracted to and that either way it was okay and not because of anything his uncle did. After the examination the boy said, "I thought this was going to be the worst day of my life, but it's the best day I've ever had."

Despite a history of anal assault, Michelle found no scarring or evidence of injury on the boy. Anal scars are so rare that some experts suggest not diagnosing any perceived abnormality as an anal scar unless the examiner has observed the acute injury or the patient has a clear history of anal bleeding and injury.

Part II

"Bunk"

Chapter 4. Common Myths

Merriam-Webster defines "bunk" as nonsense. It's short for "bunkum" which means "foolish or untrue words or ideas." Unfortunately, many of our beliefs regarding sexual assault have been steeped in bunkum for centuries. In this section, we hope to dispel many of the erroneous ideas most of us have been taught to believe are facts. We cannot know and understand the real facts regarding sexual assault so long as they remain clouded in confusion and misperception.

Let's start with a short self-test. Decide whether each of the following statements is true or false:

1. The hymen can be injured through sports, horseback riding, or gymnastics.
2. Virgins should not use tampons.
3. Girls can be born without a hymen.
4. A properly trained medical doctor can tell if a girl has been vaginally penetrated because her hymen will no longer be intact.
5. The hymen is usually broken and bleeds during first intercourse or penetration.
6. Masturbation frequently injures the hymen.
7. Anal penetration often leaves scars or laxity of the anus.
8. A large vaginal opening is a good indicator of sexual penetration.
9. An injured hymen never heals.
10. A properly trained medical doctor can often determine through an examination whether the penetrating object was a finger or a penis or something else.

Notice that, with the exception of #7 regarding the anus, all of the statements target our understanding of female genitalia. For the most part, male anatomy is open and obvious. There are few adults who would not be able to identify the penis, testicles and scrotum on a male adult or child. Female anatomy, on the other hand, is neither open nor obvious. Even some medical doctors cannot correctly and consistently label the parts of the female anatomy in Illustration 2a in Part 1. We continue to teach our children that everything "down there" on a girl is "the vagina." The vagina is the birth canal. Most of us will live our entire lives without ever seeing anyone's vagina, including our own or that of an intimate partner.

To further complicate matters, before science developed the ability to test DNA, the only reliable means for a man to ensure that a child was his legitimate heir was to marry a woman who had been protected from potential intimate contact with any other man and to continue to restrict her accessibility once married. It has only been in the last century that women have been recognized as people rather than property. Honorable men have had a genuine interest in believing that they could tell whether or not they had married a virgin by whether or not there was blood on the sheets on their wedding night. Sadly for these men and their wives, blood on the sheets has nothing to do with a woman's sexual purity.

Despite a persisting belief to the contrary, there is not nor has there ever been a membrane covering the vaginal opening to rupture or remain "intact." This, like each of the 10 statements above, is a myth. The hymen is a collar or semi-collar that surrounds the opening of the vagina but does not cover it. The hymen is just one part of the female genitalia. It must have an opening to allow secretions and menstrual blood to drain out of the vagina. The hymen does not "pop" like a balloon when an object such as a penis is inserted.

There are different shaped hymens, and a child's developmental stage can affect the appearance of the hymen, just as there are different shaped penises, and a child's developmental stage can affect the appearance of the penis. But medically speaking, a doctor might just as well examine the penis (and foreskin if it has not been surgically removed) of a young man to see if it has ever penetrated a vagina, as examine the vagina and estrogenized hymen of a young woman to see if it has ever been penetrated.

Michelle recalls being consulted in one Indiana case in 2003 where a physician had examined a young girl and concluded, "As far as virginity there appears to be no hymen, but I cannot infer how long she has been without a hymen." Armed with that medical opinion, the defense attorney deposed the girl in order to determine when she had lost her hymen. The following questions and answers are taken directly from the girl's discovery deposition:

Q. This other man put his penis inside of your vagina?
A. At the time, I didn't know what was happening, but as I look back, that's what it would have—it felt like.
Q. You were age nine (9) at this time?
A. Um-hm (affirmative response).
Q. Did you still have your hymen?
A. I don't know any of this stuff. I'm sure I did. I....
Q. It was the membrane just on the inside of your vagina?
A. What would cause me to not have it?
Q. Possibly horseback riding, falling from a bike, an injury.
A. I don't know.

Even today, victims are placed under oath and asked impossible questions based on the myths and misconceptions enumerated at the beginning of this chapter. We will address each one individually, and have included a list of peer-reviewed medical references in Appendix C for those who wish to research these facts for themselves.

1. The hymen can be injured through sports, horseback riding, or gymnastics.

Hymens can be injured, but not through normal athletic activities and not without the person realizing it. Sports injuries, including straddle injuries, almost never involve the hymen because it is protected by the labia in the same way the anus is protected by the buttocks. In fact, the hymen is further recessed and enjoys more layers of protection than the anus. It's never going to be injured during a sports activity where the participant is conscious, but unaware that any injury occurred. If it did happen, you would know it! In addition, there would be a clear history, often with many witnesses. When an injury to the hymen is observed, a changing history is a red flag: It was the balance beam, or maybe it was the bed, or possibly the bike....

2. Virgins should not use tampons.

If the normal use of tampons injured the hymen or somehow affected the virginity of the user, you had better believe there would be a warning on the tampon box, as well as on the instructions inside the box. The next time you are in a grocery store or drug store, go to the feminine hygiene section and read the warnings posted on boxes of tampons. Or if you'd rather not spend time in public reading the fine print on tampon boxes, go to the product websites.

Playtex® specifically addresses this issue on its website like this: "Q: Will using a tampon cause me to lose my virginity? A: No. You don't have to worry about losing your virginity when using a tampon. You will remain a virgin until you have sexual intercourse."
(http://www.playtexplayon.com/first-time-users/how-to-use)

The brand o.b.® gives an even more complete answer: "Will I lose my virginity if I use tampons? No. A woman can only lose her virginity by having sexual intercourse. The hymen has a natural opening in it and is made of elastic tissues that stretches [*sic*]. The natural opening allows menstrual fluid to escape from the vagina and also allows a tampon to be inserted without causing trauma to the hymen."
(http://www.ob-tampons.com/faq/good-to-know)

Tampax® says, "Please note that tampons do not affect virginity. A virgin is someone who has not had sexual intercourse."
http://www.tampax.com/en-us/tampon-information/daughter-chat/how-to-talk-to-your-teen-daughter-about-puberty.aspx

Kotex® is more vague: "[T]alk it over with your parent or other responsible adult before trying a tampon for the first time, as it may require a little practice."
(http://www.kotex.com/na/articles-info/first-period-qa/10301)

For more information on the elasticity of the hymen and virginity, please refer to Chapter 2 on Female Anatomy.

3. Girls can be born without a hymen.

The hymen is a remnant of the vagina's (birth canal's) hollowing out into a tunnel during fetal development. The only way a girl could be born without a hymen is if she were born without a vagina. There have been many studies, all confirming that all vaginas include a hymen at birth. One involved the examination of more than 25,000 newborn girls, and every one of them had a hymen. As explained in Chapter 2, not all hymens look the same. Some are like a ring (annular), while others are more crescent-shaped (crescentic). Some don't have the normal opening and require surgery (imperforate); others are almost fringe-like (fimbriated or estrogenized). Any time there is a report that the hymen is missing or a girl was born without a hymen, you can be sure that the problem lies in the observer's understanding rather than in the child's genitalia.

4. A properly trained medical doctor can tell if a girl has been vaginally penetrated because her hymen will no longer be intact.

The term "intact" should never be used when describing a girl's hymen. The hymen is like a ring or a collar around the entrance of the vagina that becomes elasticized by estrogen in puberty. By the time a girl begins menstruating, the hymen is elastic enough to accommodate a tampon, a speculum, a penis— even a baby—without injury. In fact, one study referenced in Appendix C demonstrated that 94% of pregnant teenage girls have no evidence of injury to their hymen. (Peer-reviewed article entitled "Genital anatomy in pregnant adolescents: 'normal' doesn't mean 'nothing happened'" by Kellogg, Menard and Santos).

Any time a medical provider opines that the hymen is "intact" or no longer "intact," that opinion is based on myth and misunderstanding rather than medical fact. Doctors can often see a girl's hymen and observe whether there are any signs of injury. In those cases where injury is observed, the doctor should give a detailed description of the injury. Doctors cannot tell whether a young woman with no injury has been vaginally penetrated any more than they can tell if a young man's uninjured penis has ever penetrated a vagina.

5. The hymen is usually broken and bleeds during first intercourse or penetration.

The hymen is not a barrier blocking entrance to the vagina. There is no need to "break" it. The hymen may stretch like a rubber band, but it never snaps like a rubber band. As a girl approaches puberty, estrogen elasticizes the hymen so that it can stretch. Of course, any tissue can be injured by blunt force trauma. Without proper lubrication, sexual intercourse is just as likely to cause injury or bleeding on the second, third or hundredth time as it is the very first time.

6. Masturbation frequently injures the hymen.

Let's be honest. People masturbate because it feels good. Girls are no more likely to injure themselves during masturbation than boys are. Stimulation tends to focus on the source of greatest pleasure—the penis for boys and the clitoris for girls. We might just as well worry about a boy injuring the back of his scrotum during masturbation. Is it possible? Yes. But it's not very likely.

7. Anal penetration often leaves scars or laxity of the anus.

Anal penetration is no more likely to leave scars or cause laxity of the anus than the passing of a large stool. All of us, and even our children, have passed stools large enough to clog a toilet, but with little or no injury to the anus. The anus is designed to open and close, and neither the passing of a stool nor penetration of a penis or object the size of a penis will necessarily cause injury. Depending on the penetrating object and lubrication, there can be injury. But it is impossible to tell whether it is an "entrance" or "exit wound." In other words, a large stool passing through the anus could cause the same type of injury as a similarly sized penis or object penetrating the anus.

8. A large vaginal opening is a good indicator of sexual penetration.

This is simply not true. There have been some studies that suggest a correlation between obesity in children and a slightly larger vaginal opening with less hymenal tissue, but there has been no correlation between sexual penetration and the size of the vaginal opening on a young woman. The idea that a penis becomes smaller through repeated use makes as much sense as the vagina becoming larger through repeated use. Sexual intercourse need not alter a young woman's genitalia any more than it alters a young man's. There is no correlation between the size of the opening of the birth canal and whether or not digital or penile penetration has occurred.

9. An injured hymen never heals.

Most acute or fresh injuries that we observe can and usually do heal completely. There is no "scarring" of tissue like you might see after an injury to your skin. The membrane of the hymen is similar to that in the roof of your mouth. Have you ever burned the roof of your mouth biting into a hot slice of pizza? It hurts for little while, but heals very quickly without any accumulation of scarred tissue.

Still, a visible, healed injury to the hymen is very rare and usually appears as a transection (missing tissue all the way to the base of the vagina) or a cleft/notch of missing tissue rather than a "scar." Unless the hymen has been observed prior to the injury and confirmed in two positions, however, it can be difficult to say whether the appearance of a cleft or notch is "normal" or evidence of blunt force or penetrating injury.

10. A properly trained medical doctor can often determine through an examination whether the penetrating object was a finger or a penis or something else.

Even when there is a fresh injury observed, a medical provider can describe the type of injury (blunt force, penetrating) but cannot tell just by the type of injury what exactly caused the injury. This information is usually obtained through the patient history. A physician or nurse can only say whether any injury observed during the examination is or is not consistent with the history provided by the patient.

Vulva, Not Vagina

Why do these myths persist? It's been 20 years since Eve Ensler wrote "The Vagina Monologues," and we're still talking about vaginas. We tell our children that boys have penises, and girls have vaginas. Few people will go an entire lifetime without ever seeing a penis. Yet most people will never actually see a vagina. The vagina is the birth canal, an internal organ. Using "vagina" to vaguely reference everything "down there" on a female perpetuates misconceptions far beyond any feminine mystique. It would be like teaching our children that all of the "boy parts" are called the "vas deferens." The vas deferens is the tube that connects a boy's testes with his urethra allowing semen to pass through the penis. It seems ludicrous to suggest that we tell our children that boys have a vas deferens and girls have a vagina, and we're not recommending that anyone actually do that. What we are recommending is that we tell children that boys have a penis and girls have a vulva, a medically correct term describing the visible parts of a girl's genitalia. And as they approach adolescence, they need to know that sexual intercourse does not alter a woman's vulva or her vagina, any more than it alters a man's penis or his vas deferens.

Chapter 5. Defining Rape

Another common area of misunderstanding stems from the multiple meanings and interpretations of the word "rape" and added descriptors such as "legitimate rape." There is also disagreement as to whether all sexual assaults are "rape," or whether there are some, less serious, types of sexual assault which should not be included in the definition of rape. Who has the right or ability to say whether or not the conduct is rape?

First, it is important to understand that "rape" is a legal term, not a medical term. The precise elements of the crime are defined by statute, and each state has its own criminal code definition. The United States Code § 920, Art. 120 also defines rape as a federal criminal offense. There is no uniform universal definition, but the criminal statistics we gather on rape come primarily through the FBI's Uniform Crime Report (UCR) and the Justice Department's National Crime Victimization Survey (NCVS). The UCR gathers information from police departments on the number of rapes reported to the police. It does not include any rape that was not reported to the police. The NCVS surveys the random population and asks about both reported and unreported instances of rape. This gives us specific information on unreported crimes, but that information is only as reliable as the person doing the reporting and that person's understanding of what does or does not constitute rape. By looking at both the UCR and the NCVS, we gain a broader view of the rate of sexual assault. For more information on how the data is gathered and the strengths and weaknesses of each, visit the Department of Justice FBI page on UCR Statistics at http://www.ucrdatatool.gov/twomeasures.cfm. The Center for Disease Control and Prevention (www.CDC.gov) and the Rape, Abuse & Incest National Network (www.RAINN.org) are other frequently cited sources for sexual assault statistics.

Not everyone agrees on the definition of rape, and the definitions we use are continuing to evolve. Rape used to be an offense that could only be committed by a man upon a woman who was not his wife. For 80 years, the FBI defined "rape" as "the carnal knowledge of a female forcibly and against her will." It was up to each police department to determine which reported crimes under their state laws met this definition and report them to the FBI for inclusion in the UCR. In December 2011, the FBI expanded its definition to include both genders and oral and anal assaults. The new FBI definition of "rape" for UCR reporting purposes reads, "Penetration, no matter how slight, of the vagina or anus with any body part or object, or oral penetration by a sex organ of another person, without the consent of the victim." This definition is much improved from the old one, particularly in the shift from "force" to "without consent." It still misses the mark by requiring penetration of the birth canal.

In Laurie's young adult novel *Maybe I Will* (Luminis Books / 2013), three characters deal with sexual assault. Only one would be "rape" under the old FBI definition, but all three are rapes under the new FBI definition. In the book, one is labeled "hazing," one arises out of wrestling or horseplay, and one is what we traditionally call rape: forced sexual intercourse. Readers often have difficulty understanding that the mental and emotional violation that comes with being sexually assaulted by someone you know can be every bit as traumatizing as a more brutal physical violation by a stranger. The physical injuries are often the easiest to treat and the first to heal. Someone who is assaulted by a stranger can usually count on the undivided support of friends and family. Someone who is assaulted by a friend or family member, however, will often see friends and family divided in their support.

In *Maybe I Will*, two of the three assaults are reported to the police, yet none are prosecuted as crimes. Unfortunately, that is not unusual for sexual assault cases. According to the Rape, Abuse & Incest National Network (www.RAINN.org), out of every 100 sexual assaults, only 32 are ever reported to the police. Of those that are reported, only 7 will lead to an arrest of the perpetrator. Of those, only 3 will be prosecuted. Of those prosecuted only 2 will be convicted and sentenced for their crime. In other words, 98% of rapists are free to rape again.

Why do so few rapists go to prison? Because sexual assault runs a gamut of opposites, often driven by unclear facts, assumptions and innuendo. On the one side is legal, moral, consensual, pleasurable sexual contact; on the other is criminal, immoral, nonconsensual, devastating sexual contact. Our social expectation of right and wrong, our personal judgments regarding good and evil, and our individual experience of pleasure and pain are all loaded into our perceptions about sexual contact. As children growing up, we all received mixed messages regarding sex and little genuine education to help us understand our bodies, talk about our sexuality, and set healthy boundaries for ourselves and others. When a person is able to give consent, traditional social expectations required evidence of physical violence and a struggle to show that the act was not consensual. When a person is unable to give consent, society has been more apt to recognize the violation regardless of physical injury, as we do in child molestation and statutory rape cases.

At the same time, our collective definition of rape is evolving from an offense that can only be committed by a man upon a woman to any act of sexual penetration without consent. The new FBI definition is a step in the right direction, but is only one step on our journey toward justice when it comes to understanding and prosecuting rape. In our criminal justice system, "rape" is a legal conclusion to be determined by a fact-finder (jury or judge) and must be based upon proof beyond a reasonable doubt. No medical provider or witness can say that the conduct in question was or was not rape. That is a question for the jury.

Some states, like Illinois and Alaska, have eliminated the term "rape" altogether. Rather than addressing the specific statutes of all 50 states, we will look at how four different states (California, New York, Illinois, and Alaska) define rape. For a quick reference to all 50 states, visit https://www.rainn.org/public-policy/laws-in-your-state.

Rape in California

The California Penal Code §261 states: (a) Rape is an act of sexual intercourse accomplished with a person not the spouse of the perpetrator, under any of the following circumstances:

(1) Where a person is incapable, because of a mental disorder or developmental or physical disability, of giving legal consent, and this is known or reasonably should be known to the person committing the act. Notwithstanding the existence of a conservatorship pursuant to the provisions of the Lanterman-Petris-Short Act (Part 1 (commencing with Section 5000) of Division 5 of the Welfare and Institutions Code), the prosecuting attorney shall prove, as an element of the crime, that a mental disorder or developmental or physical disability rendered the alleged victim incapable of giving consent.

(2) Where it is accomplished against a person's will by means of force, violence, duress, menace, or fear of immediate and unlawful bodily injury on the person or another.

(3) Where a person is prevented from resisting by any intoxicating or anesthetic substance, or any controlled substance, and this condition was known, or reasonably should have been known by the accused.

(4) Where a person is at the time unconscious of the nature of the act, and this is known to the accused. As used in this paragraph, "unconscious of the nature of the act" means incapable of resisting because the victim meets any one of the following conditions:

(A) Was unconscious or asleep.

(B) Was not aware, knowing, perceiving, or cognizant that the act occurred.

(C) Was not aware, knowing, perceiving, or cognizant of the essential characteristics of the act due to the perpetrator's fraud in fact.

(D) Was not aware, knowing, perceiving, or cognizant of the essential characteristics of the act due to the perpetrator's fraudulent representation that the sexual penetration served a professional purpose when it served no professional purpose.

(5) Where a person submits under the belief that the person committing the act is someone known to the victim other than the accused, and this belief is induced by any artifice, pretense, or concealment practiced by the accused, with intent to induce the belief.

(6) Where the act is accomplished against the victim's will by threatening to retaliate in the future against the victim or any other person, and there is a reasonable possibility that the perpetrator will execute the threat. As used in this paragraph, "threatening to retaliate" means a threat to kidnap or falsely imprison, or to inflict extreme pain, serious bodily injury, or death.

(7) Where the act is accomplished against the victim's will by threatening to use the authority of a public official to incarcerate, arrest, or deport the victim or another, and the victim has a reasonable belief that the perpetrator is a public official. As used in this paragraph, "public official" means a person employed by a governmental agency who has the authority, as part of that position, to incarcerate, arrest, or deport another. The perpetrator does not actually have to be a public official.

(b) As used in this section, "duress" means a direct or implied threat of force, violence, danger, or retribution sufficient to coerce a reasonable person of ordinary susceptibilities to perform an act which otherwise would not have been performed, or acquiesce in an act to which one otherwise would not have submitted. The total circumstances, including the age of the victim, and his or her relationship to the defendant, are factors to consider in appraising the existence of duress.

(c) As used in this section, "menace" means any threat, declaration, or act which shows an intention to inflict an injury upon another.

It's a long and complicated statute, and we include it in its entirety only to demonstrate how complicated and convoluted the laws can be. The statute essentially says an act of sexual intercourse with someone other than your spouse is rape if accomplished by force or on a person unable to consent. Rape of a spouse (§262), sexual intercourse with a minor (§261.5), and other sexual assaults (Sodomy §286; Oral Copulation §288A, and sexual penetration by a foreign object §289) are all addressed as separate crimes in California that are not legally called "rape."

Rape in New York

New York Penal Law §130.35 provides in relevant part:

A person is guilty of rape in the first degree when he or she engages in sexual intercourse with another person:
1. By forcible compulsion; or
2. Who is incapable of consent by reason of being physically helpless.

As in California, other forms of sexual assault are covered by other specific statutes, but are not technically defined as "rape."

Rape in Illinois

The crime of "rape" no longer exists in Illinois. Instead, what used to be the crime of rape now falls under Criminal Sexual Assault.

720 ILCS 5/11-1.20 states in relevant part that (a) A person commits criminal sexual assault if that person commits an act of sexual penetration and:
    (1) uses force or threat of force; [or]
    (2) knows that the victim is unable to understand the nature of the act or is unable to give knowing consent;

"Sexual penetration" means any contact, however slight, between the sex organ or anus of one person and an object or the sex organ, mouth, or anus of another person, or any intrusion, however slight, of any part of the body of one person or of any animal or object into the sex organ or anus of another person, including, but not limited to, cunnilingus, fellatio, or anal penetration. (720 ILCS 5/11-0.1).

This definition is very much like the new FBI definition of rape except that it requires force or the threat of force be used against anyone who is able to consent.

Rape in Alaska

Rape is also no longer an official crime on the books in Alaska. The crime is now "Sexual Assault," and unlike the laws in California, New York and Illinois which required the element of force, Alaska is more in line with the new FBI definition that replaces the element of force with the absence of consent.

The Alaska statute, AS 11.41.410, states in relevant portion that (a) An offender commits the crime of sexual assault in the first degree if (1) the offender engages in sexual penetration with another person without consent of that person.

When looking to define rape or sexual assault in the legal sense, you must look specifically at the statutes and case law of the state where the conduct occurs. Case law tells us how the appellate courts in that state have interpreted the language of the criminal code or statutes. You may think you understand the meaning of the words, but not all words are limited to their plain meaning or common usage. For example, under Indiana's prior statutes, using an object to penetrate the anus or sex organ of another person was specifically addressed, but digital penetration was not. Indiana case law confirmed that a finger was an object for the purpose of that statute, but you wouldn't know that just by reading the statute.

Chapter 6. Force vs. Consent

Every sex crime requires either a lack of consent on the part of the victim or the use of force on the part of the perpetrator. Too often people think that "without consent" is the same as "by force," but that is not true in a legal sense. Appreciating the difference is the first step in understanding how the justice system works and why it so often fails in the eyes of sexual assault victims. **Please note that not all rapists and child molesters are male, and not all victims are female. However, given the restraints of the English language and the fact that a majority of offenders are male, and a majority of victims are female, we will use masculine pronouns for offenders and feminine pronouns for the victim for readability and clarity.**

A Woman's Presumed Consent

Sexual assault is the only crime where victims are presumed to consent and actually have to resist physically, risking serious injury or even death, to establish their lack of consent. It's true. It's still a man's world, and our laws do more to protect a man who is careless with his wallet than to protect a young woman who trusts the wrong people.

Imagine a young man is walking down the street in a relatively safe neighborhood just after dark. He's approached by an acquaintance, and the two men chat briefly. Suddenly and without warning, the acquaintance punches him in the stomach and tries to take his wallet. A neighbor sees what happens, asks if he's okay and offers to call the police.

Now imagine a young woman is walking down the street in that same relatively safe neighborhood just after dark. She's approached by the same male acquaintance, and the two chat briefly. Suddenly and without warning, he grabs her, kisses her and shoves his hand down her pants. A neighbor sees what happens, yells for them to "take it inside" and threatens to call the police.

Even if the woman reports the sexual assault immediately, the jury is going to want to know what she was doing out after dark, what she was wearing, and whether she "wanted it," things that would matter very little or not at all with regard to the young man in the robbery attempt. They would never believe a defendant who says that his victim wanted to be punched in the stomach and robbed, but many would believe a defendant who says that the woman wanted the sexual contact, but then experienced "buyer's remorse" once she knew the neighbor saw her.

A Man's Presumed Innocence

On top of the woman's presumed consent, the man is presumed innocent. Our legal system is founded on the premise that it's better for a hundred guilty men to go free than for one innocent man to be wrongly convicted. Every reasonable doubt, every piece of missing evidence, every unexplained question must be resolved in favor of the accused. The accused has the right to remain silent, and no negative inference may be drawn from the assertion of that right.

After everyone else has testified, the defendant can take the stand and make up any plausible story he can think of based upon what the jury heard. Even if he's a convicted criminal or has sexually assaulted someone before, the jury probably isn't going to get to know that information. It's too prejudicial; the jury might think that he did it this time just because he's done it before or he has broken the law in some other way.

The victim must take the stand, confront her assailant face-to-face, identify him and tell a courtroom full of people exactly what he did while he and his attorney listen and interrupt with objections to her testimony anytime they like. Then his attorney has the opportunity to ask the victim leading questions on cross-examination, questions like: You know the defendant from your neighborhood, don't you? You've attended some of the same parties and have a number of mutual friends, don't you? You were out walking alone after dark, weren't you? And you stopped to talk to my client, didn't you? You knew him and thought he was a nice guy, didn't you? In fact, even on the night in question, you were fine until the neighbor yelled at you both to take it inside, weren't you?

How "Without Consent" Differs from "With Force"

Most women who are raped (nearly 75%) actually know their attacker, and the question at issue is not who did it or whether or not there was a sexual act, but whether the woman consented or the man used force. In Indiana, if a woman can legally consent (i.e., she's old enough, has sufficient mental capacity, has not been given a date rape drug and is otherwise awake and aware), then every crime of sexual assault requires the state to prove beyond a reasonable doubt that the man used physical force or the threat of force.

Consider the scenario above. The young woman's attacker used the element of surprise more than the element of force. She might not have been able to say anything while he had his mouth over hers, and he may have stopped when she pushed him away, especially if a neighbor had called out. She didn't consent, but she couldn't say, "NO!" or "Stop!" until he'd actually done it, unless she anticipated what he was going to do. Without clear, physical force compelling her to submit to the touching, there simply may not be enough to prove a sexual assault beyond a reasonable doubt if the applicable statute requires force.

In fact, there are three equally valid responses to such a surprise attack: fight, flight and frozen fright. Two out of the three make it almost impossible to prosecute the above case. Frozen fright looks and sounds like consent. Flight undermines the element of force—all she had to do was walk away. The only reaction that clearly demonstrates a lack of consent is the one that is likely to provoke an even greater level of force by the perpetrator.

Even in cases where the woman fights her attacker off, reports the crime immediately and physical injuries are documented, defendants often claim that the victim consented to "rough sex." Or they'll apologize for the size of their "large male member" or for being an inexperienced lover, saying they never meant to hurt her or didn't realize in the throes of passion that she was experiencing pain rather than pleasure.

In these acquaintance rape cases where the victim knows her attacker, persuading twelve people—male and female, young and old—to agree beyond a reasonable doubt is a formidable task. It's no wonder victims often feel that our justice system has failed them.

From "No Means No" to "Yes Means Yes"

In the past there have been campaigns to raise sexual awareness based on the tagline "No Means No." The basic premise is that when a person clearly and vocally says "no" to an uninvited sexual advance, there should be no sexual contact. The problem with "No Means No" is that the person is free to assume anyone and everyone wants to engage in sexual conduct absent a clear and convincing statement to the contrary.

"Yes means yes" seeks to change the presumption of consent to a presumption that people do NOT want to have sex with every person they meet. Every person that I come into contact with should assume that I do not want to engage in sexual activity with him or her unless I clearly communicate that desire and we agree that it's something we both want to do.

We conduct every other area of our business and personal affairs in this way. Suppose you said you liked my shoes. It would still be illegal for me to take $100 from your wallet without your consent and leave you my shoes in return. We have to talk about the transaction and agree upon the terms, and we're all comfortable doing this. Except when it comes to sex. Most of us have been conditioned as children that we should NOT talk about sex, even as we're inundated with sexual messages for the purposes of marketing and entertainment.

Colleges are an excellent place to educate people on how to talk about sex in a meaningful way and establish healthy boundaries in intimate relationships. Too often young heterosexual men assume that the answer is "yes" until she says "no," while young heterosexual women assume that the answer is "no" until she says "yes." The law sides with the aggressor, and society blames the victim. Universities can and should raise awareness, provide accurate information, and empower students to move beyond the ambiguity of silence and create a world of mutual respect and communication.

This does not mean universities should become criminal investigators and prosecutors or that defendants somehow lose their constitutional presumption of innocence in criminal proceedings. Changing the element of "by force" to "without consent" does nothing to undermine defendants' constitutional rights and everything to recognize the basic human dignity of every potential victim. The difference between "force" ("No Means No") and "without consent" ("Yes Means Yes") is that juries would no longer be required by law to presume that victims consent to every sexual advance. Defendants would no longer be entitled to assume that everyone they meet wants to have sex with them.

Think again about the three natural responses to fear: fight, flight and frozen fright. If someone comes up to you holding a hand in a pocket in such a way as to look as if there is a gun pointed at you and orders you to give him your wallet, it's robbery whether or not there really was a gun. If his objective is rape rather than robbery, then you had better fight back and risk being shot. The law would never presume you want to give him your money the way it presumes that you want to have sex with him.

In 2012, Sex Educator Al Vernacchio gave an excellent TED talk entitled "Sex Needs a New Metaphor" dealing with consent by addressing a common metaphor used for sex: Baseball. He suggests that we stop making sex an adversarial competition creating winners and losers and instead approach consent for sex as we would if we were going to share a pizza. It's only about eight minutes long, and well worth the time of anyone troubled by the "Yes Means Yes" concept. It's available online at:

https://www.ted.com/talks/al_vernacchio_sex_needs_a_new_meta phor_here_s_one?language=en

Consent is...

~Willing participation
~Based on choice
~Active not passive
~Based on equal power
~Only possible when neither party is incapacitated or impaired due to drug or alcohol consumption
~Is given and not assumed
~Is not the absence of a "no"
~Is given during each experience and can be withdrawn at any point.

Consent is not...

~A drunken "yes"
~Given by anyone significantly impaired by drugs or alcohol
~Giving in because of fear
~Agreement based on threats or coercion
~Purchased
~Going along in order to gain approval
~Silence or the absence of a "no"
~Capitulation

The Legal Age of Consent

If you ask most adults in Alaska what the legal age of consent is, they would say 16. In New York and Illinois, people say 17, and in California, 18. The truth is that the age of consent differs significantly from state to state, and the answer is seldom an exact number. It is important to read and understand all of the criminal statutes that relate to child molesting, child exploitation, and statutory rape to determine whether or not an individual less than 18 years of age can legally consent to any specific type of sexual contact in any specific state.

We will use Indiana as an example. The relevant statutes define child molesting (Indiana Code 35-42-4-3) and sexual misconduct with a minor (Indiana Code 35-42-4-9). Sexual conduct with a child less than 14 years of age is child molesting. But there is no minimum age for a person to be a child molester. So any child capable of forming a criminal intent may molest a younger child. Children as young as 10-years-old have been charged with sex offenses. Case law suggests that if two 13-year-olds engage in any type of fondling or sexual intimacy, the older of the two (even if it's just by a day) is molesting the younger of the two.

Indiana's statutory rape provision suggests that the age of consent is 16 years old, and that anyone over the age of 18 who engages in sexual conduct with someone who is not yet 16 years of age commits the crime of sexual misconduct with a minor. Nevertheless, there is a "Romeo" provision which states that it is a defense if the alleged offender is not more than four years older than the victim and the two have had an ongoing dating relationship.

Neither of these criminal statutes applies to teens ages 14-17 who engage in consensual sexual activity. Although few people would answer "14" if you asked them the legal age of consent in Indiana, that is the correct answer. A 14-year-old can consent to have sex with another 14, 15, 16, or 17-year-old, and some 18-year-olds. A 15-year-old can consent to have sex with those ages 14-17, and some 18 and 19 year-olds. Once you reach the age of 16, you can consent to have sex with most adults. However, child exploitation and child seduction laws define "child" as anyone not yet 18. There are some people you can never consent to have sex with because of the power they hold over you (your jailor, for example). And it's always illegal to have sex with anyone who is your close biological relative (parent, child, grandparent, grandchild, sibling, aunt, uncle, niece, or nephew), regardless of consent.

In most states, child molesting and statutory rape crimes impose strict liability, which means that the prosecution does not have to prove that you knew the specifics of the law, and a mistake as to the age of the child is no defense. Knowing the laws in your home state is important, but if you travel with children and teenagers to other states on vacation, it is worth knowing the laws of those states as well to ensure that your child does not unwittingly become a victim or sex offender.

Grooming

There's an old urban legend that if you put a frog in a pot of boiling water, he'll naturally hop out; however, if you place a frog in a pot of cool water and gradually increase the heat, you'll end up with a cooked frog. This may or may not be true for frogs, but it certainly is true for many children who are sexually molested. The gradual cooking process is known as "grooming," and the increased heat is the evaporation of physical and emotional boundaries. The Webster's Dictionary definition of "grooming" includes "training for a particular purpose." For child molesters, that purpose is a sexual relationship.

Most people still want to believe that child molesters are deviant strangers who abduct children or entice them with candy and puppies. We teach our children to be wary of strangers, to shout "NO!" or run away and tell a trusted adult if anyone should ever approach them in such a manner. We teach them about "good touches" and "bad touches" and believe they will tell us immediately if they receive a "bad touch." Our intentions are good, but we're preparing them for the exception, not the reality of sexual abuse.

In reality, the molester is more likely to be the trusted adult and the touch is more likely to feel good. There are family members, friends and neighbors, even teachers, coaches and clergy who pay extra attention to children listen to what they are really saying and strive to meet their emotional, physical and spiritual needs as a means of fulfilling their own sexual needs and desires. The "nicer" the molester appears and the more "troubled" the child appears, the more difficult it is to detect and believe the sexual abuse.

The Grooming Process

Grooming is a perversion of romantic courting—you find yourself interested in someone, find out everything you can about him or her, see how you might fit into each other's life, spend lots of time together and eventually become physically intimate. According to former FBI agent Kenneth Lanning, there are five stages in the grooming process: 1) Identify the possible victim; 2) Collect information about the intended victim; 3) Fill a need; 4) Lower inhibitions; and 5) Initiate abuse.

1. Identifying the possible victim
Children make ideal victims. They are naturally curious, easily led by adults, need lots of attention and affection, and are seeking to establish independence from their parents. Children from broken homes and troubled families are easy targets. The more "unlovable" the child feels and appears, the less likely the child is to tell on someone who displays love and the less likely anyone is to believe the child if the child ever tells. A child recently caught stealing or lying makes a particularly appealing victim.

2. Collecting information about the intended victim
The more a molester knows about his victim, the better able he is to build trust with the child and the child's parents. He learns how the child responds to attention and praise. He displays a superficial sympathy and charm whenever the child discusses her problems and concerns. He assesses her strengths and weaknesses, taking special note of how she interacts with her friends and the other adults in her life. All of this information will be used to control the child and manipulate the people around her.

3. Filling a need
The molester exploits the child's emotional needs by freely offering love, friendship and support. Parents may even feel relieved that the child has found a responsible friend, mentor or role model or that they have found a dependable babysitter,

depending on the age of the child. Whatever the parent needs, the molester is pleased to help out. Whatever the child needs or wants, the molester is happy to provide, with or without the parents knowledge or consent. Some molesters will even instigate a sexual relationship with a single parent just to gain access to her children. The greater the family need and the molester's position of trust, the less ability a child has to say, "NO!"

4. Lowering inhibitions

Once trust is established and the victim is emotionally vested in the relationship, the molester may begin offering gifts or money to the child to see how well she can keep secrets from her parents and to make her feel special and loved. Loving gestures will begin to invade her personal space and might include more "acceptable" kisses and hugs, increased touching of the child's hands, shoulders, arms and legs, and "accidentally" brushing up against private areas.

5. Initiating abuse

Gradually, the "accidental" touching to private areas may linger and include professions of love and hints of sexual desire. By the time the touching crosses clear boundaries, the child is too afraid she might lose the relationship to object, and too ashamed of her own perceived part in inviting the abuse to tell. And honestly, human beings engage in physical intimacy because it feels good. It's very natural for the child to want it and even enjoy it.

Shame and Blame

An adult molester's ability to lie, exaggerate, minimize, rationalize and manipulate people greatly exceeds the ability of a child to sort through her fears and emotions and think reasonably about her molester. Once the child is emotionally attached to the molester, she begins to feel responsible for him and to him. She may even believe that she is as much or more to blame for the abuse as the molester is. At this point, the molester's psychological manipulations may begin to shift from positive to negative. Criticism or the "silent treatment" may replace praise and flattery. Threats may become more frequent than pronouncements of love.

Protecting Children

In cases of grooming, much of what we teach our children about sexual abuse does more to exacerbate the child's guilt and shame when they realize something is wrong than to encourage them to tell. At what point should she have shouted "NO!"? Whom should she have told? It's frightening for parents—even good parents. No wonder so many simply choose to pretend it doesn't happen or couldn't happen to their child.

How can parents protect their kids? Awareness is the first step. The second step is focusing our energy on loving our children rather than fearing potential predators. Instead of talking about "good touches" and "bad touches," model healthy physical and emotional boundaries and talk about what's "private" and what's not. Don't be embarrassed to answer kids' questions about body parts and body functions. Be very matter-of-fact and age appropriate. Let your kids know that they can talk to you about anything. Teach them the difference between "fun surprises" and "secrets" and let them know that home is a safe place to talk about our "secrets."

Kids who experience the unconditional love of their parents and feel safe in their own home develop a very good internal barometer for appropriate relationships. That's the best defense parents have against child predators who are selecting their potential victims for grooming.

Part III
The Courtroom

Chapter 7. Criminal Procedure 101

Criminal Justice: It sounds like an oxymoron. The way the system works can feel anything but just to both victims and suspects at times. Nevertheless, a basic understanding of the process and the underlying principles will help all those, innocent or not, who find themselves unwillingly enmeshed in the criminal justice system as witnesses, victims or defendants.

Criminal Investigations

Occasionally, a police officer will witness a crime as it occurs and begin an investigation immediately. In most cases, though, crimes are not investigated until someone calls and reports the crime to the police. It may be the victim, a witness or someone who has a duty to report suspected crimes like a teacher, social worker or physician. The police investigate the crime by going to the location where the crime occurred, gathering evidence, and interviewing the victim and other witnesses. At some point during the investigation, the police contact the suspect. Every suspect has the right to remain silent and the right to an attorney. The police cannot force a suspect to answer any questions.

Depending upon the specific circumstances of the case, the police may arrest the suspect on preliminary charges and attempt a custodial interview, or the police may contact the suspect at home or work and ask them to come to the police station voluntarily and give a statement. When the police arrest a suspect, the prosecutor must file formal charges within a reasonable time period. Most states and the federal government adhere to the 72-hour rule meaning that within 72 hours of a police arrest, formal charges must be filed and the defendant brought before a judge who can review the evidence and find probable cause exists that the defendant has committed the alleged crime. If formal charges are not filed, the suspect must be released from custody. This requires the police to complete their investigation and turn the case over to the prosecutor very quickly if they want to keep the suspect in jail.

In the majority of cases, the police will conduct their investigation and then send a detailed report outlining all of the evidence to the prosecuting attorney. The prosecuting attorney will review all of the evidence and decide if it is sufficient to prove specific criminal conduct beyond a reasonable doubt. Prosecuting attorneys are afforded the greatest discretion in our judicial system. They have sole authority to determine who will be charged as a criminal and what crimes they will be charged with based upon their state laws or if it's a United States Attorney, based upon federal laws.

Formal Charges

There are two ways for a prosecutor to charge a person with a crime. Charges may be brought through a grand jury indictment or by filing an information supported by a probable cause affidavit. If a grand jury is used, the prosecutor presents all of the evidence, including live witness testimony, documentation, etc., to the grand jury along with an explanation of what crimes may be applicable. A prosecuting attorney may even require one suspect to testify against another by offering immunity or an agreement not to prosecute someone for specific crimes committed in exchange for truthful testimony.

Because there is no one to present exculpatory or conflicting evidence or to cross-examine the evidence presented by the prosecuting attorney, it is often said, "A good prosecutor can indict a ham sandwich." (Of course, a ham sandwich could not possibly commit a crime, but neither does it have the benefit of being presumed innocent). Rather than assembling a grand jury to hear evidence and tender formal indictments, many states authorize the prosecuting attorney to file an indictment or information identifying the specific law that has been broken and alleging the reckless, knowing, or intentional conduct of the accused. The information must be supported by sworn testimony, usually the affidavit of a police officer, victim, or investigator setting forth the evidence that supports the allegations.

A prosecutor must present the charges and supporting affidavits to a judge who will determine whether probable cause exists to arrest the suspect and bring him to trial. Probable cause means that there is evidence to support the belief that a crime has been committed and that the suspect is the person who committed the crime. It's a much lower standard of proof than the beyond-a-reasonable-doubt standard required to convict a defendant. It is also significantly less than a preponderance of the evidence (more likely than not), the civil standard of proof.

Arrest and Pre-trial Release

Upon a finding of probable cause, the judge issues a warrant for the suspect's arrest, and the suspect becomes a defendant in a criminal action. The judge will also decide whether the defendant will remain in custody or may be released pending trial. If the crime is particularly heinous and the defendant is a danger to the community or the defendant is a flight risk, the judge may refuse to set a bond. Otherwise, the defendant has the right to be released upon posting a reasonable bond, usually a sufficient amount to ensure that he will appear in court as required and reflects the severity of the charged crimes. If the crime is a misdemeanor and the defendant has no prior criminal history, a judge may even order the defendant released upon his own recognizance (O.R.), meaning no bond is required.

A criminal defendant may know that a warrant has been issued and may turn himself in to the proper authorities. If he does not turn himself in, then the police will serve the arrest warrant and detain the defendant until he can be brought before the judge. In a high profile case, the police may intentionally serve the warrant at the defendant's place of work or another public place where the defendant is known to be. This is called a "perp walk" and can be used to ensure the alleged perpetrator is publicly accused and taken away in handcuffs. The police call the defendant by name, announce the charges, and read him his

Miranda Rights (You have the right to remain silent....) for all to see and hear.

Initial Proceedings

Once the defendant has been photographed, fingerprinted and booked into the jail, if a bond has been set he may either post a cash bond for the full amount or call a bondsperson who will accept payment of a sum certain (usually 10%) to guarantee the entire bond amount. If bond has been set at $10,000, a defendant could pay the court $10,000 cash knowing that it will be returned to him (minus any court costs, fines or restitution) when the case concludes or pay $1,000 to the bondsperson knowing that the money will not be returned and that the bondsperson will come and find him and turn him over to the court if he fails to appear for all court hearings and trial. Whenever a defendant is released pending trial, there are certain conditions he must follow to avoid being taken into custody. Such conditions include refraining from all illegal conduct and from having any contact with alleged victims of his crime.

A defendant must be brought before a judge as soon as possible after an arrest for an initial hearing or arraignment. At that time the judge formally reads the charges to the defendant and an initial plea of not-guilty is usually entered. The defendant is then given time to hire a private attorney to represent him or to meet with a public defender if he cannot afford to hire his own attorney. Defendants have the right to proceed to trial without an attorney and defend themselves *pro se*, but the complexity of criminal law and procedure makes this an extremely risky prospect. A judge who is concerned about a defendant's ability to represent himself effectively may appoint a public defender to consult with the defendant and take over the defense at any time to ensure that the matter proceeds to trial in a timely fashion and that the defendant's due process rights are protected.

Defendants have a Sixth Amendment right to a "speedy trial." The Constitution does not define "speedy," and the definition varies greatly from state to state depending upon each state's statutes and case laws. Many states specify the exact number of days from the defendant's arrest or first court appearance after arrest until the defendant must be brought to trial. In Indiana, that time period is 70 days for an incarcerated defendant and 365 days for a defendant who has been released on bail or bond. Delays requested or caused by the defendant do not count toward the 70-day or 365-day limits. Other states have no set time standards but consider the length of the delay, the reason for the delay, whether or not the defendant has specifically requested a speedy trial, and any prejudice the delay has caused the defendant. Whenever a defendant's right to a speedy trial has been violated, the remedy is the same as if the defendant had been acquitted at trial: The charges are dismissed and cannot be refiled.

Because the consequences are so extreme, prosecutors and judges must be very mindful to get criminal cases set for trial as quickly as possible and avoid delays whenever possible. Court calendars are often congested with multiple trials scheduled at the same time because most cases will resolve before trial through a plea agreement. An incarcerated defendant is given preference on the trial calendar over a defendant who is not in custody. If two trials are set for the same day and neither pleads, the case that has been pending the longest will usually be given preference. Defendants, especially those who are not in custody, frequently seek to delay their cases in hopes that witnesses will disappear or memories will fade, making the case against them less persuasive.

Discovery

A defendant is entitled to know what evidence the prosecution has to prove his guilt. Due process also requires that prosecutors disclose any exculpatory evidence that would call into question the defendant's guilt. The actual evidence that must be produced and when it must be produced is controlled by the rules of criminal procedure in each state or the Federal Rules of Criminal Procedure in federal court. Many states require that each side provide the other with a list of those who will be called to testify at trial, and depositions are sometimes scheduled to discover what a witness's testimony will be. Discovery depositions are also used to preserve a record of that witness's testimony. Sometimes it takes months or even years for a case to go to trial. Memory fades and perceptions change. The deposition can be used to make sure that witnesses' accounts of events don't change significantly at trial.

A deposition is a recorded statement given under oath before a court reporter who transcribes the testimony into a written document with page numbers and lines for easy reference. The party taking the deposition gets to ask questions first. Opposing counsel can make objections for the record. There may be some discussion on whether or not the witness should be required or permitted to answer a question. Witnesses are generally not part of those discussions and should remain quiet until the attorneys agree that the question should or should not be answered.

Sometimes by the time the discussion is over and a decision is made about answering the question, the witness will have forgotten what the question was. Witnesses should never answer a question that they don't remember, or didn't hear, or didn't understand completely. Instead, they should politely request that the attorney who is asking the question repeat it, or restate it, or clarify it as needed. Ultimately, it is the judge who decides what questions must be answered and whether those answers are admissible at trial. Judges do not attend depositions. Nevertheless, attorneys do sometimes call judges in the middle of a deposition to get a ruling on whether or not a witness can be compelled to answer certain questions.

Motions to Suppress Evidence

Defendants can allege that their constitutional rights were violated during the criminal investigation of the case. For example, if the police stopped the defendant while driving and searched the vehicle without any probable cause that the person had committed a crime, any evidence obtained during that search may be excluded from trial. Knowing that any evidence obtained in violation of a defendant's Fourth Amendment rights discourages police officers from conducting illegal searches and seizures. Another common example is if a defendant was not properly advised of his rights before he confessed during an interrogation. The defendant's confession and even the fact that he has admitted to committing the crime may be suppressed, or excluded from being presented to the jury at trial.

When a defendant files a motion to suppress evidence, the judge will set a hearing to determine what evidence was obtained and how it was obtained. If the police violated the defendant's constitutional rights, the judge must determine exactly which evidence is attributable to that violation and whether or not the evidence might have been discovered anyway. The judge's decision on what evidence will be admitted at trial and what evidence will be suppressed can greatly affect the outcome of the criminal case. If the suppressed evidence is the only evidence that the judge used in finding probable cause existed to arrest the defendant or to support the charges against the defendant, the judge may dismiss the case.

Even if the judge does not dismiss the case, the prosecuting attorney may decide to dismiss the charges if it seems unlikely that there will be sufficient evidence at trial to prove the case beyond a reasonable doubt. Such dismissals are without prejudice, meaning that the case may be refiled at a later date if further investigations result in additional evidence obtained legally and without violating the defendant's constitutional rights. If the defendant has been charged with multiple crimes, the prosecutor may decide to dismiss the charges that relied upon the excluded evidence and proceed with the remaining charges. Or the prosecutor may choose to proceed with the criminal charges as filed, but offer a more favorable plea recommendation.

Guilty Pleas vs. Jury Verdicts

Knowing what evidence will be admitted at trial encourages the defendant and prosecutor to engage in plea negotiations, allowing both sides to agree upon a specific result rather than letting a jury decide the facts and a judge decide the sentence. Plea agreements offer some benefit to defendants, but they also benefit society, victims and witnesses. In fact, the vast majority of criminal cases are resolved by a guilty plea rather than a jury trial. The time and expense of a criminal trial, not to mention the number of courtrooms and personnel it would take to try every case, would make a jury trial in every case impossible. Where the evidence is not genuinely in dispute, it makes sense for both sides to agree upon a reasonable legal outcome. A plea of guilty frequently benefits the victims who will not be forced to appear at a deposition or in trial, face their assailants and be cross-examined on their testimony. Also, a defendant generally cannot appeal a conviction based upon his own plea of guilty as easily as he can appeal a jury verdict of guilty, so there is less opportunity for the conviction to be reversed by a higher court.

Victims are entitled to be heard, but do not in and of themselves have the power to "press charges" or "drop charges" against their perpetrators. That power lies within the prosecuting attorney's discretion.   Although defendants have the right to remain silent and cannot be forced to testify, victims and witnesses can be compelled to testify. Refusal to appear or to testify fully and truthfully may result in criminal contempt charges or perjury charges against the witness.

If the case proceeds to trial and a jury finds the defendant "not guilty" then the case is over. If the jury returns a verdict of guilty, the defendant has the right to appeal that decision. Appeals can take years and may result in having the verdict set aside and having to try the case all over again. The State may appeal a decision to clarify the law as determined by the trial judge, but the only remedy is for the law to be applied correctly in future cases. Once a not-guilty verdict has been entered, double jeopardy prevents the defendant from being prosecuted again for that crime. In other words, a conviction can be reversed on appeal, but once a defendant is acquitted of a crime there can be no reversal of that decision. He can be charged with any new crime he commits, but he cannot be charged for the same conduct or same incident again.

The 18th century English jurist William Blackstone wrote, "It is better that ten guilty persons escape than that one innocent suffer." Benjamin Franklin said it is better one hundred guilty persons should escape than that one innocent person should suffer. Blackstone and Franklin were referring exclusively to those who are accused of crimes. Their victims are not counted among the innocent persons who suffer. And while innocent people suffer at the hand of criminals every day and innocent people are sometimes wrongly accused of criminal conduct, our government cannot take any person's life or liberty without due process of law.

Chapter 8. Collecting Evidence

There are three crime scenes in a sexual assault: the location where the sexual assault occurred, the victim's body and the perpetrator's body. It is up to law enforcement to collect evidence from the crime location. The history provided by the patient during a sexual assault examination can help the police know what corroborating evidence may exist and where to look for it. Unless the perpetrator is caught in the act and/or immediately taken into custody, any injuries inflicted by the victim in self-defense may heal and any of the DNA from the victim or other trace evidence on the suspect's body will be lost. As a suspect, the perpetrator has the absolute constitutional right to remain silent, but with probable cause prosecutors can request a search warrant to collect a DNA sample and fingerprints from the suspect and a search warrant for the premises where the assault occurred. Investigating the crime scene and the suspect's body are outside the scope of this book.

This chapter will focus on the victim's body as a crime scene and the SANEs ability to collect forensic evidence during the sexual assault examination of her patient. The two types of evidence most law enforcement officers, prosecutors and jurors want to see are physical injuries and the suspect's DNA. The truth is that physical evidence in genital, anal and oral penetration cases is rare. 90- 95% of sexual assault patients present with no physical injuries, and there is no way for a SANE to know during the sexual assault examination whether or not she is collecting the suspect's DNA from her patient's body.

First, let's look at why there are so many cases where the SANE finds no injury and the result of the exam is "normal." Often, based upon the history of the assault, the SANE would expect to find no injury, and the fact that there are no visible injuries is completely consistent with the patient's history of sexual assault, especially for children who have been groomed (see Chapter 6). If the perpetrator is a trusted adult, there is less of an inclination to inflict pain or injury on the child because it increases the risk of the child telling what happened to someone who may report it. Rather than engaging in vaginal coitus, the penetration may have been vulvar coitus, rubbing the penis between the labia rather than inserting it fully into the vagina. With proper lubrication, not only does this not inflict pain or injury on the child, it stimulates the clitoris and may feel very good to the child.

SANEs should always ask whether the patient experienced pain or bleeding during or after the event. When talking with children, it's important to use whatever words the child uses for genitalia. SANEs ask children focused questions about pain and bleeding, but avoid leading questions that suggest specific details (Did it hurt? Did you bleed?). Common focused questions include: How did that make your "pee pee" feel? Did you see or feel anything in your underwear or on the sheets? How did your "private" feel when you went to the bathroom?" If the patient does not report any pain or bleeding, then the SANE would not expect to see any evidence of physical injury.

Even when there is a report of pain or bleeding, the female sex organ (FSO) is very vascular and heals quickly. Sometimes the history indicates that enough time has passed for the injury to have healed. It is similar to burning the roof of your mouth on a hot slice of pizza. It hurts and/or burns initially, but the pain goes away in a matter of hours and leaves no scar. Even if there is no visible injury remaining, if the patient reports a burning sensation the first time she urinated following the assault, this may be (absent evidence of any other cause) evidence of penetration of the FSO. The stream of urine passes over the internal portion of the FSO and a burning sensation suggests that there was at least some small abrasion or irritation inside, indicating that the penis, finger or object was "in" rather than just "on" the FSO. In adolescents and adults, the hymen is estrogenized and naturally stretches to accommodate a penis or similar-sized object with little or no injury regardless of consent or force.

When there are visible injuries, the SANE photographs them and notes them on the chart. If the patient has consented to genital photographs, all genital injuries are also photographed. If a speculum is to be used in the exam it is important to document all visible genital injuries or the fact that there are no visible genital injuries before inserting the speculum. Sometimes the question arises as to whether a specific injury might have been caused by inserting a speculum rather than by the defendant. Careful observation and documentation along with a commitment to "do no harm" enable a SANE to reply to such inquiries with confidence and credibility.

SANEs identify trauma such as blunt force, sharp force, penetrating trauma, or a combination of these. Common terminology also includes abrasion, laceration or tear, cut or incision, bruise or contusion, hematoma, swelling or edema, redness or erythema, and petechiae. SANEs look for and document defensive injuries based upon the patient's history of the assault. SANEs should also look for pattern injuries. For example, an injury in the shape of a seat belt fastener may corroborate a patient's history of sexual assault in a car. Accurately recording a patient's height and weight may also be relevant to issues regarding force. If the suspect is 6'0, 250 pounds while the patient is 5'0 and 100 pounds, then the suspect lying on top of the patient suggests much greater force than if a 5'0, 100-pound suspect lies on top of a 6'0, 250-pound patient. A patient may gain or lose weight, and a child may grow significantly from the time of the assault to the time of the trial. An accurate record of the patient's height and weight at the time of the assault can be significant evidence at trial.

It is also important for patients with documented injuries to return for a follow-up examination so that the SANE can confirm that the injuries have healed. A follow-up exam may also reveal that a discoloration that appeared to be an injury is actually a normal variant for this patient. SANEs identify and confirm physical findings using multiple methods such as alternate positions, labial separation and traction, colposcopic visualization, Foley catheter technique, peer review and expert consultation.

Rape Kit

Our SANEs use a state-approved "rape kit" to collect forensic evidence, including DNA evidence and trace evidence (fibers and hair), that can be sent to a laboratory for testing. Careful documentation of what exactly is collected and from where on the patient's body is critical as is careful handling of the evidence to maintain the chain-of-custody until it is picked up by law enforcement. A photograph of Indiana's rape kit and some of the tools used at the FWSATC is included as Illustration 8a. The actual collection of evidence is based upon the patient history, advanced training and anywhere an alternate light source (ALS) illuminates as potentially containing a suspect's body fluid and DNA. The rape kit is a tool to be used, not a recipe to be followed.

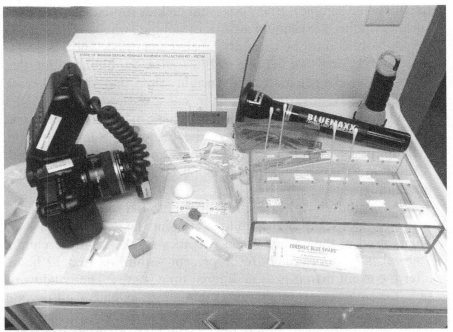

Illustration 8a

Perhaps the most important aspect of evidence collection is to prevent evidence transfer or contamination. If a SANE picks up one piece of evidence (like underwear) and then another piece of evidence (like a shirt) she can unintentionally transfer evidence from the first item to the second item. If she handles an item without wearing gloves, she may inadvertently transfer her own DNA or fingerprints onto the item. The exam room and equipment must be cleaned using appropriate methods and exam paper must be replaced for each exam. The SANE should use gloves or plastic forceps to touch items that may contain fingerprints and change gloves any time there is a risk of evidence transfer. The SANE must know what she is doing and why she is doing it, clearly document all findings and note any deviations from normal procedures. Wet samples are collected with dry, sterile Q-tip swabs while dried specimens of suspected blood, semen and saliva must be collected using a double swab method (using a sterile wet swab to moisten the area followed by a sterile dry swab to collect the sample). Bite marks and hickies (bruises caused by sucking on the skin) should always be double swabbed.

All swabs must be carefully labeled and dried. The FWSATC uses swab dryers like the one in Illustration 8a, but anything that keeps the swabs separated and upright while they dry will work (modeling clay, inverted Styrofoam cups, tissue boxes). SANEs always use paper bags, not plastic. Plastic bags retain heat and moisture in a way that destroys the evidence. Some rape kits include paper envelopes that require moisture to be sealed. SANEs must never lick the envelope because that contaminates the samples.

When the patient is a child, the most likely place to find a suspect's DNA is on the child's clothing and any blankets or linens used at the scene. When it comes to DNA on the child's body, it is far more likely to be present within the first 12 hours after the event than it is as additional time passes. The window of time for emergency and urgent examinations extends well beyond that to ensure that forensic evidence is collected whenever it might still be present. In addition, DNA technology continues to change and improve in ways that makes it worthwhile to err on the side of swabbing and collecting all potential evidence. The perpetrator may attempt to conceal his DNA by using a condom or having the patient wash or douche to remove all traces of evidence. Historically, the FWSATC has recovered the most DNA from children's necks where the assailant has breathed heavily, licked, kissed or perspired and also from children's upper, inner thighs.

Collecting Suspect Standards

The FWSATC does not collect suspect samples or perform suspect examinations. However, there are places where victims and suspects are examined in the same facility, perhaps even by the same examiner. It is better to use separate facilities and different examiners whenever possible, but if the available resources simply don't allow it, then special care must be taken to avoid cross-contamination. Use different exam rooms and be sure that the examiner changes gowns, and gloves and documents all precautions taken to keep the evidence from the patient completely separated from the suspect's evidence.

It is important to establish up front that an examiner who is also a medical provider is collecting forensic evidence exclusively and will not be diagnosing or treating the suspect in a way that establishes a provider-patient relationship. If the suspect presents voluntarily for the forensic examination, written consent should be obtained, but a separate form should be used rather than a standard patient consent form because the suspect is not a patient. More commonly, a court order or search warrant will have to be issued for the collection of specific pieces of evidence. The details of how such examinations will be handled must be coordinated with law enforcement in advance. The suspect may not refuse a court-ordered examination, and the forensic examiner is acting as an agent of law enforcement. Asking questions of suspects may violate their 5th Amendment right to remain silent. Law enforcement must be present at all times and handle the custody and restraint of any suspect who becomes uncooperative, hostile or violent. These and other potential issues need to be clearly worked out before doing any suspect exams.

The Rios Case

Michelle recalls two highly publicized Indiana cases where the evidence collected by a SANE had a significant impact on the outcome of the criminal charges and convictions and also exonerated a teenager who had been implicated in an assault and prevented future attacks by a very dangerous man. The first was the Simon Rios case, where a young girl was abducted, raped and murdered. The second case was the Michael Jent case, where a young girl was abducted, raped and released.

On December 8, 2005, 10-year-old Alejandra disappeared from her bus stop. The local newspaper headline suggested she "Vanished in thin air." Five days later, Simon Rios, a member of that same Hispanic community, murdered his wife and three young daughters, one of whom was Alejandra's classmate. While Rios was in custody for killing his family, he gave police information that led to the discovery of Alejandra's frozen body near a gravel pit 50 miles south of Fort Wayne. Rios also implicated a 17-year-old boy in Alejandra's abduction and murder. The forensic pathologist who performed the autopsy invited Michelle to attend and assist in the collection of evidence. The injuries observed and DNA evidence recovered confirmed that Alejandra had been sexually assaulted as well and that it was Simon Rios, not the teen, who sexually assaulted her. Rios pled guilty to raping and murdering Alejandra and was sentenced to multiple, consecutive life sentences for his many atrocious crimes. On October 9, 2008, Rios hanged himself in his prison cell.

The Jent Case

On August 29, 2004, an 8-year-old girl was walking with her 5-year-old brother in Fort Wayne, Indiana. A man approached them asking for help to find his puppy and forced the girl into the car. He took her to an abandoned home and released her one hour later near where he had picked her up. The girl remembered scant facts: She saw a wall along the roadway. There was no furniture in the home and no water. The police had no leads, and the two children gave differing descriptions of the suspect and the vehicle.

The girl was taken to the FWSATC for a sexual assault examination two hours after the assault. She described penile oral, anal and vaginal assault, telling the SANE (as recorded on her patient chart): "he you know raped me, said if I yell he'll kill me, he licked down there and put lotion on his dick just to get it in more, he made me suck him, he had sex with my butt too, He stuck his hands inside my crotch and butt, I was bleeding when I went to the bathroom, said he wanted to make babies with me, put lotion on me to stop bleeding, he put it on my butt too. It hurt."

During the sexual assault examination, the SANE observed no physical injuries in the head-to-toe examination and no active bleeding anywhere. The anal exam revealed three small anal tears and the genital exam revealed scattered petechiae on the hymenal ring. Using a standard Rape Kit from the State of Indiana, the SANE swabbed the girls mouth, combed trace evidence out of the girl's hair, scraped under her fingernails, swabbed the external FSO, performed and retained a washing of the internal FSO, and swabbed the girl's anus. Based on the history the girl provided, the SANE also swabbed her neck, hands, calves, and butt cheeks and collected the clothing (shorts, shirt and underwear) that the child was wearing.

The girl returned three days later for a follow up exam. At that time the exam was completely normal. The anal fissures and hymenal petechiae had healed completely, leaving no trace of her injuries. The police had no leads, so the case went cold. Meanwhile, the rape kit and clothing were sent for DNA analysis. The suspect's DNA was found in only one place: On the girl's neck. That DNA was sent to CODIS and matched the DNA of Michael Jent, a Fort Wayne man who had been convicted of a Burglary in 1997. Jent's DNA on the young girl gave the police probable cause to obtain a search warrant for an empty home owned by Jent's family. At that home the police collected a washcloth that was also sent for DNA analysis and found to contain both his DNA and the girl's DNA. They also found an enema bottle with Jent's thumb print on it. When the police arrested Jent, he had a rope, large garbage bags, lubricant and duct tape in his car trunk. But for the neck swab collected during the sexual assault examination, Jent would have remained free to find his next victim.

Chapter 9. Testifying in Court

In all criminal cases, including sexual assault cases, the burden is on the prosecution to prove every element of the State's charges against the defendant beyond a reasonable doubt. Prosecutors do this by presenting evidence at trial. This evidence can be in the form of an exhibit (the gun the defendant carried, a photo or video of the crime scene, the clothes a victim was wearing, the defendant's hand-written statement, etc.) or in the form of testimony from a witness. The judge decides what witnesses may or may not say based upon the Rules of Evidence. Each state adopts its own Rules of Evidence. The Federal Rules of Evidence are fairly representative of the controlling rules in most states, so they will be cited here.

Direct and Cross-examinations

The prosecutor calls the witness who must swear or affirm the truth of the testimony to be given, and then the prosecutor begins asking questions. This is the direct examination of the witness, and the Rules of Evidence require that the questions be non-leading, ensuring that the substance of the testimony comes from the witness in his or her own words rather than from the attorney asking the questions. Non-leading questions are the who, what, when, and where, designed to elicit the facts of the case, often followed by questions like "And then what happened?" If the prosecutor tries to lead the witness or asks what people said instead of what they did, opposing counsel may object, and it will be up to the judge to decide whether or not the witness may answer the question.

After the prosecutor completes direct examination of the witness, opposing counsel is given the opportunity to cross-examine the witness. Unlike on direct examination, the questioning attorney may use leading questions, especially yes-no questions, that state the specific points that the attorney wishes to make. Instead of asking an open question like "What time did Mr.

Jones arrive?" this is the opportunity for the attorney to ask questions like "Isn't it true that you were asleep when Mr. Jones arrived?" and "So you don't really know what time he arrived, do you?" After opposing counsel finishes with the cross-examination of the witness, the prosecution has the opportunity for re-direct, once again asking open-ended questions that allow the witness to explain in detail what happened.

Examples of both the direct and cross-examination of a SANE are included in Appendix D.

Fact Witnesses vs. Expert Witnesses

There are two types of witnesses: fact witnesses and expert witnesses. Fact witnesses can only testify to things that they know first-hand because they saw, heard, smelled, tasted, or touched something that the jury needs to know about in order to understand what happened. An expert witness is someone who has training and/or experience beyond what most people know about a subject and can offer an opinion that will help the jury understand the evidence they must consider.

Federal Evidence Rule 702(a) states, "If scientific, technical, or other specialized knowledge will assist the trier of fact to understand the evidence or determine a fact in issue, a witness qualified as an expert by **knowledge, skill, experience, training or education** (emphasis added), may testify thereto in the form of an opinion or otherwise." A pathologist can remove a bullet from a body and can say that in his opinion, that bullet wound was the cause of death. A ballistics expert can examine the bullet and testify that in his opinion it was fired by the gun found near the scene. A fingerprint expert can testify that in his opinion, the fingerprints found on the gun belong to the defendant. This is all expert testimony.

A SANE is often called to testify as both a fact witness and an expert witness in a rape trial. As medical providers, SANEs examine the patient and document the injuries they observe. They also collect evidence to send for DNA testing and can testify as to specifically where they found that evidence on the victim's body. These are facts within their personal knowledge based upon their examination of the patient.

They may have an opinion as to whether the injuries they observe are consistent with the history they obtained from the patient. This is expert testimony and requires that a proper foundation be laid demonstrating the SANE's experience and expertise. Any witness with professional training relevant to the criminal charges should be asked to prepare a current curriculum vitae (C.V.) in case they are called upon and able to give an opinion. The C.V. can be admitted as an exhibit to become part of the permanent case record and support any opinions offered in case of appeal.

SANEs may also testify as experts to educate the jury about the female anatomy and debunk the myths discussed in Chapter 4. They can cite the research that shows 90-95% of known pediatric sexual assault examinations (perpetrator confessed or assaults witnessed or videotaped) do not reveal physical injuries due to delayed disclosure (the injury has already healed), the use of lubrication, or the depth and angle of penetration. Most acute or fresh injuries that SANEs observe can and usually do heal completely. There is no "scarring" of tissue like you might see after an injury to your skin. Visible healed injuries to the hymen are very rare and usually appear as either a healed transection or a healed tear rather than a "scar." Unless the hymen has been observed prior to the injury, it is difficult to say whether the appearance is "normal" or evidence of penetrating injury.

Medical Hearsay Exception

One of the greatest advantages of having a treating medical provider testify at trial is that hearsay statements made to the provider during the examination are admissible at trial. Hearsay is anything anyone said outside of the courtroom being offered at trial as evidence in order to prove what was said. Federal

Evidence Rule 803(4) is known as the medical hearsay exception. It reads: "Statements made for purposes of medical diagnosis or treatment and describing medical history or past or present symptoms, pain or sensations, or the inception or general character of the cause or external source thereof insofar as reasonably pertinent to diagnosis or treatment."

In other words, any medical provider who is able to diagnose and treat a patient can testify at trial about what the patient said even though it is hearsay as long as the statements relate to diagnosis or treatment. In addition to those things specifically stated in the Medical Hearsay Exception (symptoms and inception of pain, sensations, and the cause or source of pain), medical providers may also testify regarding hygiene activity that might affect the presence or absence of forensic evidence, methods of concealment, the patient's dress and general appearance, and whether or not the patient was significantly impaired due to alcohol or drugs. At times medical providers are testifying as fact witnesses relaying what they observed in their examination of the patient. They may also go a step further and testify as experts as to what the fact finder might infer from those facts based upon the provider's education and experience. Again, having the medical provider's C.V. admitted as an exhibit helps to support any testimony that goes beyond facts and into an opinion if the case is appealed.

Nurses as well as physicians can testify under the medical hearsay exception. Although a physician is needed for differential diagnoses, nurses can and do make nursing diagnoses. To be clear, let's look at Webster's New World Collegiate Dictionary's definition of medical and medicine. Medical means "Of or connected with medicine or the practice or study of medicine." Medicine is "The science and art of treating, curing and preventing disease, relieving pain, and improving and preserving health."

Now let's look at the definition of nursing according to the American Nurses Association's Nursing Scope & Standards of Practice. Nursing is "the protection, promotion and optimization of health and abilities, prevention of illness and injury, alleviation of suffering through the diagnosis and treatment of human response, and advocacy in the care of individuals, families, communities, and populations." Mosby's Medical, Nursing & Allied Health Dictionary, sixth edition, defines diagnosis as the "identification of a disease or condition by a scientific evaluation of physical signs, symptoms, history, laboratory test results, and procedures. Kinds of diagnoses are clinical diagnosis, differential diagnosis, laboratory diagnosis, nursing diagnosis, and physical diagnosis."

Nurses are medical providers. They are autonomous practitioners and are accountable for all aspects of their practice, for judgments made and actions taken or not taken in the course of their nursing practice. Their regulatory body requires and expects RNs to formulate a nursing diagnosis and treat patients. Details of common diagnoses and treatments are discussed in detail in Chapter 1. SANE nurses need to include their nursing diagnosis on their charts to demonstrate that they did rely upon the patient's history to formulate a nursing diagnosis. See the FWSATC charts and forms included in Appendix A.

Child Hearsay

For the medical hearsay exception to apply, patients must know that they are talking to a medical provider who will be examining them for diagnosis and treatment. We believe adults understand what doctors and nurses do and the need to tell them the truth for medical diagnosis, but courts have become more reluctant to believe that children understand this concept. As a result, there has been a trend requiring attorneys to lay a more extensive evidentiary foundation for the medical hearsay exception to apply to children. The evidence must demonstrate that the child knew she was talking to a doctor or nurse, understood what the doctor or nurse was going to do, and the importance of telling the doctor or nurse what really happened with all the parts of her body. Such a foundation can usually be introduced through the medical providers if they document their examination of children consistently and are asked the right questions on direct examination. (See Appendix D).

Preparing to Testify

Witnesses may be called to testify at a hearing before the judge, at a deposition or at trial. The prosecuting attorney or the defense attorney (or sometimes both) will send you a subpoena commanding you to appear at a specific time and place. If the time or place is a problem, you need to call the attorney immediately to see if the date and time of the subpoena can be changed to better accommodate your schedule.

The subpoena may be a regular subpoena that compels you to appear in person and answer questions under oath, or it could be a subpoena *duces tecum* which, like a regular subpoena, compels you to appear in person and answer questions, but also requires you to bring specific documents with you. Make sure that you have all of the requested documents available. If the request includes documents that you don't have or don't think you should have to produce, you may need to consult with your own attorney or ask the Prosecutor to file an objection to those parts of the subpoenaed documents. It would then be up to the judge to decide whether or not the requested documents must be provided.

In addition to any documents that you're requested to bring with you, you may also want to review other documents or things. For example, you may want to review your calendar to ensure that you have the correct dates and times for events. You may also want to review any report that you generated, or any handwritten notes or journals that might help refresh your memory. It is important to do what you can to ensure your testimony is accurate and correct, but keep in mind that the attorneys may have the right to see any documents you have reviewed to help you prepare to testify according to Federal Evidence Rule 612 and similar state rules.

Testifying

Witnesses are usually called to testify in person at the trial. Occasionally, if the parties know in advance that a witness will not be available at the time of trial, an evidentiary deposition will be taken in advance of trial to be used at trial. Evidentiary depositions are frequently used for doctors' testimony, expert testimony or the testimony of a witness who is in the military or will be leaving the country for an extended period of time. The deposition may be videotaped and played for the jury at trial or a written transcription of the testimony that can be read to the jury at trial. If it wasn't videotaped, then the attorney who took the deposition will find someone to read the part of the witness. That reader will often sit in the witness stand and the attorney who asked the questions in the deposition will read the questions asked and the reader will read the answers given, so that the jury can receive the testimony almost as if the witness were there.

If you are a professional called upon to testify at any hearing, evidentiary deposition or trial, you need to dress professionally and conduct yourself professionally while you are on the stand. Remember, none of this is actually about you. You are simply there to convey some relevant information to the jury for their consideration. It is the attorney's job to ask the right questions and the judge's job to rule on opposing counsel's objections. Your job is only this: Listen to the question. Answer the question. Wait for the next question.

Regardless of what you think of the attorneys, the defendant, or the victim, answer the questions with the same professional demeanor regardless of who is asking them. Answer each question honestly. Remember you are under oath. Sometimes, especially on cross-examination, an attorney will ask you a yes or no question and want only a yes or no answer. If you can answer honestly with a yes or no, then you must do so. Hopefully, the other attorney will give you the opportunity to explain with more detail after the cross-examination has concluded and there is an opportunity for the other side to ask questions in redirect examination.

If you are asked a yes/no question, that cannot be answered honestly with a simple yes or no, you can turn to the judge and say that neither a "yes" or a "no" by itself would be true without some qualification or explanation. But you must maintain your professional demeanor and be respectful when you address the judge. Even if an attorney asks questions in a very argumentative or accusatory tone, don't let it rattle you. Just listen to the question, answer the question to the best of your ability, and wait for the next question.

Keep in mind the difference between the answers "I don't know" and "I don't recall." For example, when being asked about what happened or specific details about your observations, "I don't know" suggests that even if you'd asked me that in the middle of the event I'm describing, I wouldn't be able to tell you. It is completely outside what I was able to see, hear or observe first hand. "I don't recall" suggests that if you had asked me the question as the event was unfolding or immediately afterward, I could have answered the question. Now that the event has passed, I do not recall the information that you are requesting.

An example might be, "Were the patient's stud earrings gold or silver?" This is something you could have observed while you were there with the patient and could probably have answered, but it wasn't a detail that you documented or recall independently. If there had been something unusual about the earrings, say one was gold and the other silver, you might have recorded or even still recall that fact independently. Compare that to a question like, "Did her father give her the earrings she was wearing?" That is not something that you could see or otherwise know for yourself. Unless you were there when her father gave her the earrings, you don't know. It is better to say, "I don't know" than "I don't recall." Even if she told you that her father gave her the earrings, you don't have any personal knowledge of that fact. It's hearsay. Whether or not that comes in depends upon whether it fits within an exception to the hearsay rule, such as the medical hearsay exception that we discussed earlier in this chapter.

The rules on what is admissible evidence at trial and what is not admissible are very complicated and often require a ruling by the judge on whether the probative value of the evidence outweighs any unfair prejudice to the defendant. This is why you should never try to "help" the attorneys by slipping in extra information beyond what is asked for by the question. Often there is a good legal reason that they are not asking about some things. The court may have granted a motion in limine that prevents attorneys from talking about certain things like the victim's sexual history or the defendant's prior arrest. By "helping" you may actually say something that the judge believes is so prejudicial that the only remedy is a mistrial, grinding everything to a halt and requiring a new trial with a new jury all because of your statement.

What We're NOT Supposed To Talk About

When prosecutors and defense lawyers are thinking about the evidence they intend to present to the jury at trial, it helps to know in advance whether the judge is going to admit or exclude certain evidence. A motion in limine is a motion filed before the trial begins and asks the judge to rule on whether or not specific evidence is going to be admitted. These are things that the jury would definitely want to know, but that may be unfairly prejudicial in a way that causes them to jump to conclusions instead of basing their verdict on the facts of this case alone. Two standard motions in limine are one by the prosecutor instructing the defense not to talk about the victim's prior sexual conduct and one by the defense attorney instructing the prosecution not to bring up any prior bad acts by the defendant.

The prosecutor's motion asks the judge to enforce what are known as "rape-shield" laws. The idea behind a rape shield law is that the victim of a sexual assault is not on trial and should not be subjected to questioning about her past sexual experiences, how she dresses or her behavior outside of her experience with the defendant. In the past, the criminal justice system offered significantly more protection to women who were perceived to be virtuous. Now the Federal Rules of Evidence, Rule 412, and similar state rules and statutes limit the admission of such evidence. But as with most rules, there are exceptions which can vary from state to state, and even if there is a preliminary ruling by the judge that the victim's prior sexual experience will not be admitted, there is still the possibility that the prosecution will "open the door" for such evidence to come in at trial. An example would be if a victim testifies that she would never have sex with a man she just met at a bar when in fact she has done that before, then every instance where she had picked up a man in a bar and had sex with him would become relevant to her credibility as a witness.

Likewise, a defendant who has been accused of or convicted of sexual assault in the past does not want a jury to know about that because it would make it much easier for them to convict him in his current case. Federal Rule of Evidence 404 prohibits using a defendant's prior crimes, wrongs, or other bad acts to suggest that the defendant committed the crimes he's accused of. If the defendant is a convicted rapist, then the jury might think that, regardless of the evidence in this case, the defendant probably raped this victim, too. Such inferences would violate the defendant's right to a fair trial. But this rule also has its exceptions, which may vary slightly from state to state. Evidence of a defendant's prior bad acts may be admissible for other purposes, such as proving motive, opportunity, intent, preparation, plan, knowledge, or identity. There are usually rules that require the prosecutor to provide ample notice of the possibility that such evidence may be introduced if the "door is opened" by the defense.

For example, Laurie recalls a child molest case where the defendant had been convicted of molesting the victim's older half-sibling a decade before. The defense filed its motion in limine prohibiting the introduction of that conviction under Indiana Rule of Evidence 404(b). The judge granted that motion saying that the jury should not know about the defendant's prior conviction. In that case, the defendant waived his 5th Amendment right to be silent and testified not only that he did not molest the victim, but that he could not have molested her because he was never alone with her in the house. That testimony by the defendant "opened the door" for Laurie to call his older daughter to testify that he had molested her repeatedly when her mother and siblings were in the house in another room or asleep. The older daughter's testimony became relevant to the issue of opportunity, when the defendant told the jury that he had no opportunity to molest his younger daughter.

Usually when a motion in limine has been granted, the attorneys are required to instruct their witnesses not to mention whatever evidence the order excludes. As a witness, however, it is impossible to know all of the issues that have been raised and argued in advance and what may or may not cause a mistrial. Sometimes when a witness mentions something that violates the defendant's constitutional rights, the judge will simply instruct the jury to disregard the statement and admonish them that they must not consider it when they deliberate on the facts of the case. Other times, the information may be so prejudicial that such an instruction and admonition is insufficient. The only remedy is to start over with a new trial.

More Testifying Tips

What can you do if you're called to testify at trial to ensure that you do not cause a mistrial? **Listen to the question that is asked. Answer that question (and only that question). Wait for the next question.** If the question seems designed to elicit inadmissible evidence, then opposing counsel will object. Resist the temptation to keep talking after an attorney has made an objection. Wait until the judge rules on the objection. If the judge sustains the objection, you are not to answer the question. Just wait for a new question. If the judge overrules the objection, then you need to answer the question. If you're not sure you can ask the judge, "Do you want me to answer that question?" If, after all of the objections and argument you are not sure exactly what the question was, ask to have the question repeated.

Don't be sarcastic. The transcript won't capture your sarcastic tone and your response may be misinterpreted on appeal. Don't argue. Only the lawyers are getting paid to argue. Never, ever interrupt or talk over the judge. The judge has the authority to find you (and anyone else in the courtroom, including the attorneys) in contempt if your behavior is inappropriate or disrespectful or if you refuse to comply with a direct order of the Court. If the judge finds you in contempt, you can be fined or escorted off to jail or both. This seldom happens, and there is almost always an advance warning, where the judge gives you a very specific instruction and warning, for example: "You need to sit down and be quiet or I will find you in contempt."

Testifying can get emotional, so it helps to remember that this is not about you. The defendant is the one accused of a crime and on trial. At the end of the day, you will be free to go home. It also helps to remember the purpose of direct and cross-examination and what the attorneys are trying to accomplish through your testimony. In the SANE direct examination sample questions provided in Appendix D, you can see how the questions lay a foundation to establish the nurse as a competent, credible witness. The prosecutor wants to establish her professional qualifications and have her C.V. outlining all of her credentials and experience admitted as an exhibit.

During the direct examination the SANE explains what she does and why she does it. She talks about the standard procedures, guidelines and forms that are used in sexual assault cases. This gives the jury a foundation of knowledge and prepares them to hear about what the nurse did in this particular case. But before moving to the actual facts of the case in question, the prosecutor needs for the jury to know what a sexual assault nurse examiner is, what she does, why she does it, and also what she does not do and why she does not do it. When the direct examination moves to the specific facts of the case in question, the jury will understand with more clarity what the SANE did and why she did it.

Direct examination uses open-ended questions that allow the witness to explain in her own words what she knows. When

Michelle testifies, she often turns to the jury and explains important concepts to them directly, maintaining good eye contact and checking for understanding. Other witnesses may be more comfortable looking at the attorney who asked the question.

Compare the open ended questions of direct examination to the leading questions of cross-examination. Cross-examination is opposing counsel's chance to testify to the facts that most favor the defendant. Attorneys keep a tight rein on witnesses in cross-examination, often allowing for only a short, single-word answer from the witness. The attorney's purpose is to create doubt about the witness's qualifications, or her objectivity, or what she was supposed to do, or what she actually did, or what she should have done but didn't do. In short, the defense attorney's job is to make things less clear and create reasonable doubt.

After the defense attorney cross-examines the witness, the prosecutor has the opportunity to ask additional questions on redirect examination. Appendix D does not include a redirect examination, but the questions would need to be open ended questions and afford the witness the opportunity to explain and clarify things that might have been confusing during cross-examination. Redirect examination is the prosecutor's opportunity to restore the jury's confidence in the witness's testimony. The questions are designed to allow the witness to complete answers in context, clarify any yes or no responses and avoid any misperception, misunderstanding or misleading inferences. Cross-examination is limited to things discussed on direct examination, and redirect is limited to the testimony given on cross. Seldom will a judge allow attorneys to delve into new topics on cross or redirect examinations.

Conclusion

Statistics indicate that one in four girls and one in six boys will be sexually abused before they reach their 18th birthday. Every two minutes someone is sexually assaulted in the United States. Most of these victims will be too humiliated and too afraid to report the crime to the police, especially in cases where the attacker was a friend or family member—someone they trusted. It can take years for these victims to disclose the assault. The longer they wait, the less likely it seems that people will believe them. Sometimes they test the waters by disclosing only a small part of what actually happened to see how others will respond. If they are believed and supported they may feel safe enough to disclose the full extent of their experience. If they are not believed or are blamed, not only will they stop telling, they may even feel pressured to retract what they did say to try to win back the support of friends and family. Those who do report sexual assault are all too often treated as if they are lying or did something to deserve it. They are made to feel as if they could have done more to prevent the attack; they should have fought harder and even risked serious injury or death rather than allow themselves to be sexually assaulted.

The legal hurdles to reporting, prosecuting and actually obtaining a conviction that stands up on appeal in sexual assault cases leave the vast majority of sexual assault victims without a favorable legal outcome, no matter how competent and dedicated the Sexual Assault Response Team is. Frustration with the system can sometimes make people want to circumvent it entirely and pursue their own form of vigilante justice. Violating a defendant's constitutional rights does nothing to help or protect victims. Instead, the better we understand the unique legal and medical aspects of these cases, the more likely we are to achieve justice in our criminal proceedings and to help those who have been sexually assaulted focus on the medical and mental health outcomes that are within their control and leave criminal justice to the courts.

Our emphasis in this book has been on what happens after a sexual assault has occurred. As a society, though, we must become more proactive, raising awareness and encouraging genuine change.   Too often we direct our prevention efforts toward those we perceive as potential victims, telling them how they might avoid being raped, as if the victim is the responsible party and the one in the best position to prevent sexual assault. We direct little or no preventative effort toward potential rapists. We forget that sexual assault is not about sex. It's about power and control. Sex is neither the motive nor the objective of the rapist. Instead, sex is the weapon. And it's still a very powerful weapon in our society, protected by silence and shame on the one hand, exploited by the entertainment industry and the marketplace economy on the other.

Power in relationships is rarely absolute. There can be some shifting back and forth, and a snapshot of a single event offers little insight into the true relationship dynamics. This is why stranger rapes are always the easiest to report and prosecute. There is no history before the snapshot we see of the crime and no lingering personal connections beyond that snapshot. The evidence tends to be less he said/she said and more easily corroborated. But we know that the vast majority of sexual assaults are not perpetrated by strangers. Teaching our children how to avoid stranger danger and teaching women how to protect themselves from strangers do little to keep them safe and more to keep them silent when they are assaulted. The people most likely to assault them are the people they know and the people they trust. We must teach those with power to be trustworthy and respect the human dignity of those with less power.

Asking victims to stop sexual abuse is like asking the poor to solve the problem of poverty or the enslaved to end slavery. The only way to prevent rape is to stop ignoring and excusing the conduct of rapists. Normalizing sexism and exploitation is demeaning to both men and women. Sexual assault, like poverty and slavery, is not a women's issue or men's issue, but a humanity issue. The vast majority of rapists are men and the vast majority of their victims are women and children precisely because our society has traditionally empowered men and disempowered women and children. Everything in our culture that objectifies women and keeps them in their traditional subservient place furthers the current rape culture, intimate partner violence and sex trafficking. When it comes to sexual assault, perpetrators and victims cross gender lines, but they never cross power lines. The person with the most power is the perpetrator, and the person with the least power is the victim.

It's time to fix the brokenness in our society that perpetuates sexual assault. It is not just the victims or even the perpetrators that are broken. Healing and change will come from grassroots efforts to educate and nurture ourselves so that we may better educate and nurture our children. Together we can become the bamboo forest, ready to stand together and able to bend without breaking.

Appendices

A. 1-5 FWSATC Charts

B. NANDA Nursing Diagnoses

C. Resources

D. Direct and Cross-examination Questions for SANE

Appendix A

FWSATC Charts

These charts belong to the FWSATC and are not to be copied or reprinted without express written permission. All Rights Reserved.

Appendix A-1 Adult Medical Forensic Examination Chart

Note that there are two separate sheets provided for p. 6. The SANE selects one or the other depending upon the gender of the patient.

Appendix A-1 Adult Medical Forensic Examination Chart

FORT WAYNE SEXUAL ASSAULT TREATMENT CENTER

Adult Medical Forensic Examination

<u>**GENERAL INFORMATION:**</u>

Location of Medical Forensic Examination: _____

FWSATC Case #: _____   Law Enforcement Case #: _____

Patient Name: _____

Address _____ City _____ State _____ Zip Code _____

Patient Consent:

1. I understand that a medical forensic examination done for the purpose of nursing diagnosis and treatment plan may also include collection of samples/specimens that will be conducted by a Forensic Nurse Examiner (FNE). I further understand that I may withdraw my consent at any time for any portion of the examination. The withdrawal of my consent will not prevent the release of the examination report completed prior to withdrawal or the release of any samples/specimens obtained prior to the withdrawal of consent.

    Patient/Parent/Guardian Initial_____

2. I understand that this examination is being performed for the purpose of injury identification and collection of samples/specimens if indicated, and a referral for further medical treatment if needed.

    Patient/Parent/Guardian Initial_____

3. Photographs may be taken which may include the genital area. These may be used for medical evaluation and treatment and/or legal purposes.

    Patient/Parent/Guardian Initial_____

4. I understand that these photographs may also be used for educational purposes and if so the patient's identity will remain confidential.

    Patient/Parent/Guardian Initial_____

5. I understand the examination report and any or all samples/specimens obtained will be released to the appropriate agencies, which may include but not limited to law enforcement authorities and/or Department of Child Services (in the case of minors).

    Patient/Parent/Guardian Initial_____

6. I am:

    _____ an individual who is an adult (at least 18 years of age).

    _____ a natural parent or legal guardian of the patient.

    _____ Other _____

    Patient/Parent/Guardian Initial_____

Appendix A-1 Adult Medical Forensic Examination Chart

AUTHORIZATION:

I, do hereby, give my consent for the Forensic Nurse Examiner (FNE) to complete a medical forensic examination on myself and/or minor child. I certify that I have read, understand and agree to the conditions as described on page one (1) and do hereby release the FWSATC and its directors, officers, employees, and agents from any liability that may result from the release of the information.

_____   _____
Signature of Patient or Legal Parent/Guardian   Relationship to Patient

<u>AUTHORIZATION FOR MEDICAL FORENSIC EXAM:</u>

I request a medical forensic examination and collection of samples/specimens (if applicable) for suspected assault of the adult/adolescent at public expense.

_____   _____
Law Enforcement/Department of Child Services (Print)   Agency and ID #

_____   _____
Law Enforcement/Department of Child Services (Sign)   Date

<u>MEDICAL FORENSIC EXAM PERFORMED BY:</u>

_____   _____
Forensic Examiner (print)   Assisting Personnel (print)

_____   _____
Forensic Examiner (sign)   Assisting Personnel (sign)

_____
Date/Time

<u>LAW ENFORCEMENT OFFICER AND/OR DEPARTMENT OF CHILD SERVICES:</u>

I have received the form originals and all medical forensic samples/specimens collected by the FNE.

_____   _____
Officer (print)   Agency and ID #

_____   _____
Officer (sign)   Date/Time

Patient Name _____ FNE Initials _____ FWSATC # _____

Page 2 of 7   FWSATC

12/14 AM

Appendix A-1 Adult Medical Forensic Examination Chart

Post sexual assault hygiene activity:

	YES	NO			YES	NO	UNK
Urinated	☐	☐		Condom	☐	☐	☐
Defecated	☐	☐		Jelly	☐	☐	☐
Genital Wash/Wipe	☐	☐		Foam	☐	☐	☐
Bath/Shower	☐	☐		Gloves	☐	☐	☐
Douche	☐	☐		Mask	☐	☐	☐
Removed/Inserted				Washes self	☐	☐	☐
Tampon	☐	☐		Washes patient	☐	☐	☐
Pad	☐	☐		Clean scene	☐	☐	☐
IUD	☐	☐		Other_____			
Brushed Teeth	☐	☐					
Nose Blown	☐	☐					
Smoked	☐	☐					
Drank or rinsed mouth	☐	☐					
Eaten	☐	☐					
Vomited	☐	☐					
Changed Clothes	☐	☐					

Physical pain and/or injuries during and/or after assault_____

_____

Patient dress during assault (describe) _____

_____

Patient ☐ Alcohol ☐ Drugs ☐ No ☐ Unsure_____

Lapse of conscious ☐ Yes ☐ No _____

Other_____

General appearance of patient_____

_____

Describe condition of clothing _____

_____

Miscellanous_____

_____

_____

_____

_____

_____

_____

_____

_____

_____

_____

_____

Patient Name _____FNE Initials _____ FWSATC # _____

Appendix A-1 Adult Medical Forensic Examination Chart

B/P _____ T _____ P _____ R _____ HT _____ WT _____

Allergies _____

Medications_____

Medical History/Surgeries _____

_____

LMP: _____   Consensual A / O / V intercourse within last 4 days (Circle all that apply) N/A

Last Tetanus_____ Hepatitis B _____

Patient History:

_____
_____
_____
_____
_____
_____
_____
_____
_____
_____
_____
_____
_____
_____
_____
_____
_____
_____
_____
_____
_____
_____

Patient Name _____FNE Initials _____ FWSATC # _____

Appendix A-1 Adult Medical Forensic Examination Chart

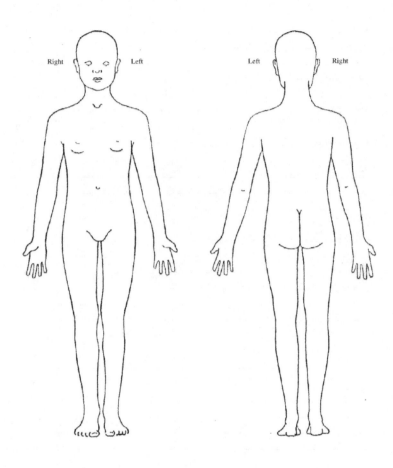

Appendix A-1 Adult Medical Forensic Examination Chart

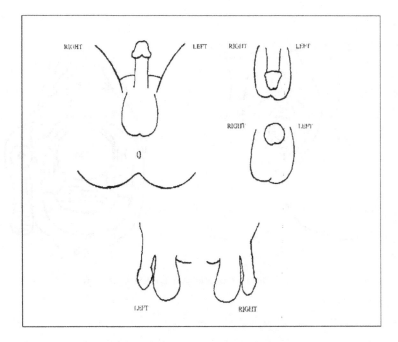

DESCRIPTION OF MEDICAL FORENSIC FINDINGS

Penis _____

Urethra _____

Scrotum _____

Perineum _____

Anus _____

Patient Name _____ FNE Initials _____ FWSATC # _____

Appendix A-1 Adult Medical Forensic Examination Chart

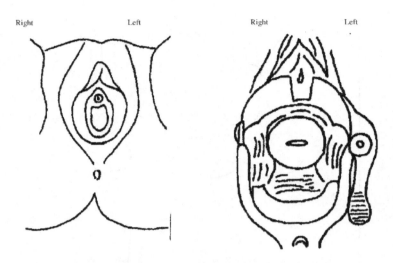

DESCRIPTION OF MEDICAL FORENSIC FINDINGS

Labia Majora _____

Labia Minora _____

_____

Urethra _____

Hymen _____

Vagina _____

Cervix _____

Perineum _____

Anus _____

Patient Name _____ FNE Initials _____ FWSATC # _____

Page 6 of 7   FWSATC

12/14 AM

Appendix A-1 Adult Medical Forensic Examination Chart

FORT WAYNE SEXUAL ASSAULT TREATMENT CENTER

ADDENDUM

_____
_____
_____
_____
_____
_____
_____
_____
_____
_____
_____
_____
_____
_____
_____
_____
_____
_____
_____
_____
_____
_____
_____
_____
_____
_____
_____
_____
_____

Patient Name _____FNE Initials _____ FWSATC # _____

12/14 AM

Appendix A-2 Adult Discharge Instructions

Appendix A-2 Adult Discharge Instructions

FORT WAYNE SEXUAL ASSAULT TREATMENT CENTER

Adult Discharge Instructions

NAME:_____ FWSATC#_____ DATE_____

DRUG ALLERGIES:_____ LMP:_____

YOUR CARE TODAY INCLUDED:
- ☐ Assessment of physical injury
- ☐ Medication administration and/or recommendations
- ☐ Pregnancy testing – urine pregnancy test result   N/A   negative   positive
- ☐ Prevention of pregnancy - Plan B
- ☐ Collection of forensic samples/specimens
- ☐ Other_____

TREATMENT PLAN:

IF AT ANY TIME IN THE NEXT 48 HOURS YOU EXPERIENCE SEVERE PAIN, CHEST PAIN, ONGOING NAUSEA/VOMITING, OR ANY OTHER UNUSUAL MEDICAL COMPLAINTS, PLEASE SEE YOUR FAMILY DOCTOR IMMEDIATELY OR GO TO THE NEAREST EMERGENCY DEPARTMENT.

☐ **Care of Injuries:** _____

☐ **The following are nursing diagnoses pertaining to your treatment plan:**
  - ☐ Acute Pain
  - ☐ Risk of Infection
  - ☐ Risk of Post Trauma Syndrome
  - ☐ Other: _____

☐ **Prevention of *Gonorrhea (GC)*:**
  - ☐ You were given Rocephin 250mg IM in a single dose
  - ☐ You were given Zithromax 1 gram (2 pills) by mouth in a single dose
  - ☐ You were given Cipro 500mg by mouth in a single dose (Need to follow up with family doctor – is not CDC approved)

☐ **Prevention of *Chlamydia*:**
  - ☐ You were given Doxycycline 100mg. Take one pill by mouth every 12 hours for 7 days until gone. Take 1st pill at _____ a.m./p.m. Take a 2nd pill at _____ a.m./p.m.
  - ☐ You were given Zithromax 1 gram (2 pills) by mouth in a single dose

☐ **Prevention of *Gonorrhea (GC) AND Chlamydia*:**
  - ☐ You were given Zithromax 2 grams (4 pills) by mouth in a single dose (Treats both Gonorrhea and Chlamydia)

☐ Contact your family doctor to make an appointment for follow-up for sexually transmitted infection testing and for original complaint(s). Call your family doctor if any new symptoms occur such as fever, genital/rectal pain, sores or discharge, urinary symptoms (painful urination, blood in urine, frequency of urination), changes in menstrual cycle (unusual bleeding, from the vagina, late menstrual cycle, and vaginal discharge. Contact Susie **(260) 449-3509** or Kathy **(260) 449-3021** at the Department of **Health (DOH)** or your family doctor to schedule an appointment for STI testing. If/when you call to schedule an appointment at the Department of Health, be sure to let them know you were referred by the Fort Wayne Sexual Assault Treatment Center. *To avoid infecting any partner with a sexually transmitted infection, we recommend that you do not have sexual intercourse until your family doctor or the Department of Health has completed an examination with cultures if necessary.*
  - ☐ Now due to findings of medical forensic exam and medical history provided
  - ☐ 2 weeks from date of medical forensic exam
  - ☐ 3 – 4 weeks from date of medical forensic exam

☐ **Prevention of HIV:**
  - ☐ We are recommending you contact your family doctor or go to the nearest emergency room **NOW** to discuss risks, concerns and options for the treatment of HIV. Treatment **must** be started within 72 hours from the time of the assault.

Appendix A-2 Adult Discharge Instructions

☐ **Prevention of Hepatitis B:**
    ☐ Contact your family doctor or go to the nearest emergency room **NOW** to discuss risks, concerns and options for the treatment of Hepatitis B. Treatment **recommended** to be started within 24 hours from the time of the assault.

☐ **Tetanus and Diphtheria Toxoid**
    ☐ Booster dose of Tetanus and Diphtheria Toxid (Td) 0.5ml given IM due to injury and patient history of more than five years since last booster dose.

☐ **Prevention of *Pregnancy*: Plan B Emergency Contraception**
    ☐ Take one pill only as soon as possible and within 72 hours of incident.
    ☐ Pill given at _____ .
    ☐ Pill must be taken within 72 hours of incident before expiration date and time of _____
    ☐ Not Given--Reason _____

☐ **Referral for Medical Consultation/Treatment:**
    I understand that I have been instructed to seek medical consultation/treatment at facility of my choice.
    ☐ Immediately _____
    ☐ Within one month for a general physical if needed, or sooner should medical problems or concerns arise.
    ☐ If you do not get your period in 2-5 weeks.

☐ **Follow up counseling and guidance is highly recommended and should be arranged. Please call:**
    ☐ Any counselor of your choice, we advise you to contact your insurance provider to see a full list of providers in your network.
    ☐ Fort Wayne Women's Bureau at (260) 424-7977
    ☐ Rape Crisis Center (260) 426-7273

☐ **Return to the Fort Wayne Sexual Assault Treatment Center on** _____
for a follow-up examination or please call (260) 423-2222 to set up an appointment. If no one is available to answer the phone, please leave a phone number or instructions on how and when you would like us to contact you. **THIS IS CONFIDENTIAL.**

☐ **Discussion of feelings common after sexual assault.**

☐ **Review information/medical sheets available in your discharge packet.**

☐ **Visit our website www.fwsate.org for additional information and resources.**

☐ **Miscellaneous instructions:** _____
_____
_____

I understand this information: _____
                             (Patient or guardian signature)

IF YOU HAVE ANY MEDICAL QUESTIONS REGARDING YOUR CARE TODAY, PLEASE CONTACT
THE FORT WAYNE SEXUAL ASSAULT TREATMENT CENTER

Forensic Nurse Examiner (260) 423-2222   Law Enforcement case #

Appendix A-3 Pediatric Medical Forensic Examination Chart

Note that there are two sheets provided as page 4. The SANE selects which one to use depending upon the age and development of the patient. Likewise, there are two sheets provided as page 5. The SANE selects which one to use depending upon the gender of the patient.

Appendix A-3 Pediatric Medical Forensic Examination Chart

FORT WAYNE SEXUAL ASSAULT TREATMENT CENTER

Pediatric Medical Forensic Examination

GENERAL INFORMATION:

Location of Medical Forensic Examination: _____

FWSATC Case #: _____ Law Enforcement Case #: _____

Patient Name: _____

Address: _____City:_____ State:_____ Zip Code:_____

Patient or Legal Guardian Consent & Conditions:

1. I understand that a medical forensic examination done for the purpose of nursing diagnosis and treatment plan may also include collection of samples/specimens that will be conducted by a Forensic Nurse Examiner (FNE). I further understand that I may withdraw my consent at any time for any portion of the examination. The withdrawal of my consent will not prevent the release of the examination report completed prior to withdrawal or the release of any samples/specimens obtained prior to the withdrawal of consent.

    Parent/Guardian Initial_____

2. I understand that this examination is being performed for the purpose of injury identification and collection of samples/specimens and if indicated, a referral for further medical treatment if needed.

    Parent/Guardian Initial_____

3. Photographs may be taken which may include the genital area. These may be used for medical evaluation and treatment and/or legal purposes.

    Parent/Guardian Initial_____

4. I understand that these photographs may also be used for educational purposes and if so the patient's identity will remain confidential.

    Parent/Guardian Initial_____

5. I understand the examination report and any or all samples/specimens obtained will be released to the appropriate agencies, which may include but not limited to law enforcement authorities and/or Department of Child Services (in the case of minors).

    Parent/Guardian Initial_____

6. I am:

    _____ natural parent of the patient.

    _____ legal guardian of the patient.

    _____ Other _____

    Parent/Guardian Initial_____

Appendix A-3 Pediatric Medical Forensic Examination Chart

AUTHORIZATION:

I, the legal custodial parent/guardian, give my consent for the Forensic Nurse Examiner (FNE) to complete a medical forensic examination on the child. I certify that I have read, understand and agree to the conditions as described on page one (1). I, the parent or legal guardian, release the FWSATC and its directors, officers, employees, and agents from any liability that may result from the release of the information.

_____   _____
Signature of Patient or Legal Parent/Guardian   Relationship to Patient

AUTHORIZATION FOR MEDICAL FORENSIC EXAM:

I request a medical forensic examination and collection of samples/specimens (if applicable) for suspected assault of the child at public expense.

_____   _____
Law Enforcement/Department of Child Services (Print)   Agency and ID #

_____   _____
Law Enforcement/Department of Child Services (Sign)   Date

MEDICAL FORENSIC EXAM PERFORMED BY:

_____   _____
Forensic Examiner (print)   Assisting Personnel (print)

_____   _____
Forensic Examiner (sign)   Assisting Personnel (sign)

_____
Date/Time

LAW ENFORCEMENT OFFICER AND/OR DEPARTMENT OF CHILD SERVICES:

I have received the form originals and all medical samples/specimens collected by the FNE.

_____   _____
Officer (print)   Agency and ID #

_____   _____
Officer (sign)   Date/Time

Patient Name _____ FNE Initials _____ FWSATC # _____

Appendix A-3 Pediatric Medical Forensic Examination Chart

PAST MEDICAL HISTORY:

Name of person providing past history _____ Relationship _____

Current physician(s)_____

Previous medical history _____

_____

_____

Prior overnight hospitalization _____Prior surgery _____

ER visit within the last year _____ Last Visit to Doctor _____

Current medications _____

Medication allergies _____ Food allergies _____ Latex allergy ( ) Yes ( ) No

Immunizations current _____ Last Tetanus_____Hepatitis B _____

Age at onset menses _____ LMP _____ Normal/Duration_____

Sanitary product used _____ Prior pelvic ( ) Yes ( ) No ( ) NA _____

Recent (60 days) Anal-Genital Injuries ( ) Yes ( ) No _____

PRIOR TO STARTING EXAM:

Role of nurse and the exam explained ( ) Yes ( ) No ( ) NA _____

Discussed that the nurse needs to know what happened for medical exam and treatment ( ) Yes ( ) No ( ) NA

_____

Child expressed understanding that I am a nurse and he/she is here for a medical examination and treatment

( ) Yes ( ) No ( ) NA _____

_____

_____

PATIENT HISTORY:

_____

_____

_____

_____

_____

_____

_____

_____

_____

_____

_____

Patient Name _____FNE Initials _____ FWSATC # _____

Appendix A-3 Pediatric Medical Forensic Examination Chart

PATIENT HISTORY CONTINUED:

_____
_____
_____
_____
_____
_____
_____
_____
_____
_____

PHYSICAL EXAM:

Height _____ Weight _____ T _____ P _____ R _____ B/P _____Tanner Scale _____

Urine Pregnancy   (____) Negative   (_____) Positive   (N/A_____)

What words does child use for:

Buttocks _____Female Sex Organ _____Breasts _____ Male Sex Organ _____

General Appearance of Patient _____

_____
_____
_____
_____
_____

	YES	NO	UNK	N/A		YES	NO	UNK	N/A
Urinated	☐	☐	☐	☐	Removed/Inserted Pad	☐	☐	☐	☐
Defecated	☐	☐	☐	☐	Tampon	☐	☐	☐	☐
Genital Wash/Wipe	☐	☐	☐	☐	Brushed Teeth	☐	☐	☐	☐
Bath/Shower	☐	☐	☐	☐	Smoked	☐	☐	☐	☐
Douche	☐	☐	☐	☐	Changed Clothes	☐	☐	☐	☐
Eaten	☐	☐	☐	☐	Vomited	☐	☐	☐	☐
Drank	☐	☐	☐	☐	N/A > 72 Hours	☐	☐	☐	☐

Patient Name _____FNE Initials _____ FWSATC # _____

Appendix A-3 Pediatric Medical Forensic Examination Chart

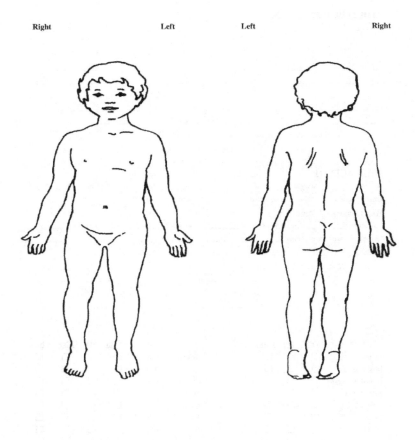

Right   Left   Left   Right

Appendix A-3 Pediatric Medical Forensic Examination Chart

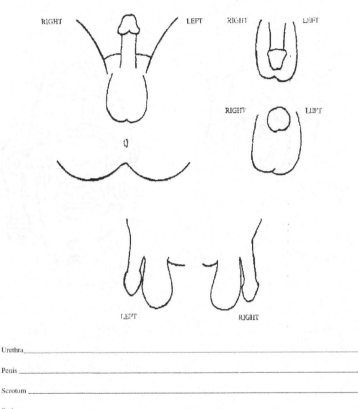

Urethra_____

Penis _____

Scrotum _____

Perineum _____

Anus _____

Patient Name _____FNE Initials _____ FWSATC # _____

Page 5 of 6

12/14 AM

FWSATC

Appendix A-3 Pediatric Medical Forensic Examination Chart

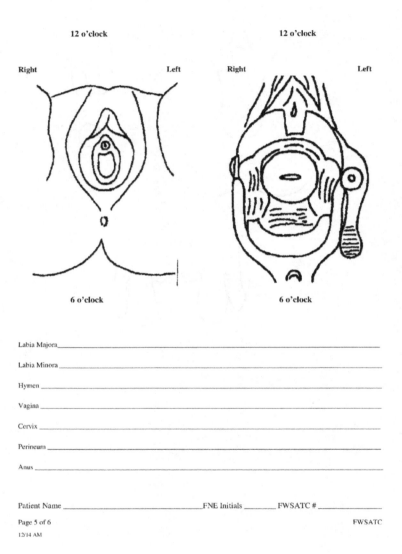

Labia Majora _____

Labia Minora _____

Hymen _____

Vagina _____

Cervix _____

Perineum _____

Anus _____

Patient Name _____ FNE Initials _____ FWSATC # _____

Page 5 of 6   FWSATC

12/14 AM

Appendix A-3 Pediatric Medical Forensic Examination Chart

Specimen Obtained	Yes	No	N/A		Specimen Obtained	Yes	No	N/A
Blood Standard					Vaginal/Cervical Swabs			
Oral Swabs					Underwear			
Neck and Ear Swabs					External Male Sex Organ Swabs			
Face/Cheek/Lip Swabs					White Drape Sheet			
Head Hair Combing								
Fingernail Scrapings								
Right Breast and Nipple Swabs								
Left Breast and Nipple Swabs								
Pubic Hair Combing					Other Clothing Items Collected			
External FSO Swabs								
Internal FSO Swabs								
Anal Folds Swabs								
Perineum Swabs								
Vaginal Wash								
Bilateral Inner Thighs Swabs								
Buttocks Swabs								

Persons present during examination: _____

Examination Narrative:

_____

_____

_____

_____

_____

_____

_____

_____

_____

_____

_____

_____

_____

Appendix A-3 Pediatric Medical Forensic Examination Chart

FORT WAYNE SEXUAL ASSAULT TREATMENT CENTER

ADDENDUM

_____

_____

_____

_____

_____

_____

_____

_____

_____

_____

_____

_____

_____

_____

_____

_____

_____

_____

_____

_____

_____

_____

_____

_____

_____

_____

_____

_____

_____

_____

_____

Patient Name _____FNE Initials _____ FWSATC # _____

12/14 AM

Appendix A-4 Pediatric Discharge Instructions

Appendix A-4 Pediatric Discharge Instructions

FORT WAYNE SEXUAL ASSAULT TREATMENT CENTER

Pediatric Discharge Information

A medical forensic examination was performed on (Name) _____
on this day _____ for the purpose of diagnosis and treatment, injury identification, and if indicated collection of forensic samples/specimens.

Your Follow-Up Appointments Are Very Important

Your child has had a medical forensic examination. **No tests** were performed that the FWSATC will call you about. The information obtained today is given to Law Enforcement and/or the Department of Child Services. A brief summary of the examination findings will be mailed to you Family doctor if authorized by a parent or guardian.

☐   Go to the nearest emergency room if at any time your child exhibits any of the following: vaginal/rectal bleeding, severe abdominal pain, lethargy, loss of consciousness, fever, dizziness, or shortness of breath. Contact your family doctor for any other non-urgent medical concerns.

☐   The following are nursing diagnoses pertaining to the treatment plan created for your child:
   ☐ Acute Pain
   ☐ Risk of Infection
   ☐ Risk of Post Trauma Syndrome
   ☐ Disturbed Body Image
   ☐ Other: _____

☐   Contact your family doctor to make an appointment for follow-up for sexually transmitted infection testing and for original complaint(s). Call your family doctor if any new symptoms occur such as fever, genital/rectal pain, sores or discharge, urinary symptoms (painful urination, blood in urine, frequency of urination), changes in menstrual cycle (unusual bleeding, from the vagina, late menstrual cycle, and vaginal discharge).
   ☐ Now because of the findings of the medical forensic exam and medical history provided
   ☐ 2 weeks from date of medical forensic exam

☐   Contact your PHCP or go to the nearest emergency room **NOW** to discuss risks, concerns, and options for the treatment of HIV. Treatment **must** be started within 72 hours from the time of the assault.

☐   Contact your family doctor or go to the nearest emergency room **NOW** to discuss risks, concerns and options for the treatment of Hepatitis B. Treatment **recommended** to be started within 24 hours from the time of the assault.

☐   Follow-up medical examination at the FWSATC is not indicated at this time.

☐   Return to the FWSATC on _____ for a follow-up medical forensic examination. **(Please call 260-423-2222 if unable to make an appointment.)**

☐   Follow-up counseling and guidance are recommended. Please continue with your current counselor or schedule an appointment with another counselor of your choice.

☐   If you have any questions or concerns please contact your Forensic Nurse Examiner _____ at the FWSATC (260) 423-2222 or visit our website www.fwsatc.org

Special Instructions: _____
_____
_____

I understand this information _____
                                                 (Parent or Guardian)

_____
Advocate

_____
Department of Child Services   (800) 800-5556

SATC # _____   LE # _____

Appendix A-5 Follow-Up Medical Forensic Examination Chart

Appendix A-5 Follow-Up Medical Forensic Examination Chart

FORT WAYNE SEXUAL ASSAULT TREATMENT CENTER

Follow-Up Medical Forensic Examination

Patient Name: _____   FWSATC Case #:_____

Accompanied by: _____   LE #: _____

Date of initial medical forensic exam: _____   Date of follow up exam: _____

Problems since initial exam: _____

_____

_____

_____

_____

_____

_____

Follow-up scheduled with Primary Health Care Provider, Board of Health, and/or counseling: _____

_____

Comments: _____

_____

_____

_____

_____

_____

No show: _____ Attempts to contact: _____

SANE Signature: _____ Date: _____

Appendix A-5 Follow-Up Medical Forensic Examination Chart

FORT WAYNE SEXUAL ASSAULT TREATMENT CENTER

Follow-Up Medical Forensic Examination

I understand the follow-up medical forensic examination will be done for the purpose of nursing diagnosis and if needed, a referral for further medical treatment. I further understand that I may withdraw my consent at any time for any portion of the examination. The withdrawal of my consent will not prevent the release of the examination report completed prior to withdrawal or the release of any samples/specimens obtained prior to the withdrawal of consent.

Patient/Parent/Guardian Initial_____

I understand that the follow-up medical-forensic examination may include photographing healing injuries and that these photographs may include the genital area.

Patient/Parent/Guardian Initial_____

I understand that any photographs taken may be used for educational purposes and if used for such purpose, the identity will remain confidential.

Patient/Parent/Guardian Initial_____

I understand and authorize the release of the examination report and any samples/specimens obtained in connection with the forensic examination to law enforcement authorities and/or Department of Child Services and/or Adult Protective Services.

Patient/Parent/Guardian Initial_____

I hereby release the FWSATC and its directors, officers, employees and agents from any liability that may result from the release of the information.

Patient/Parent/Guardian Initial_____

I am:

_____ an individual who is an adult (at least 18 years of age)

_____ a natural parent or legal guardian of the patient

Patient/Parent/Guardian Initial_____

I certify that I have read, understand and agree to the conditions as described.

_____   _____
Signature of Patient/Parent/Guardian   Relationship to Patient

Patient Name: _____   FWSATC Case #: _____

Appendix A-5 Follow-Up Medical Forensic Examination Chart

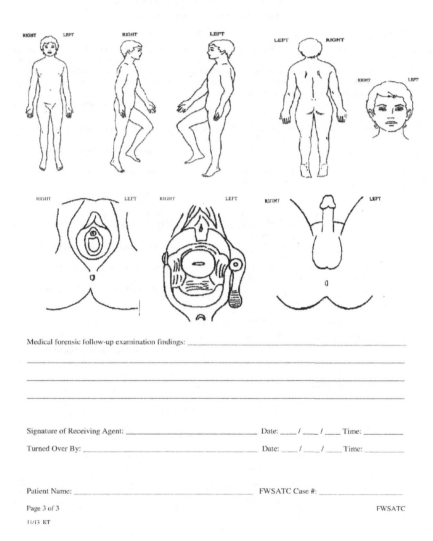

Medical forensic follow-up examination findings: _____

_____

_____

_____

_____

Signature of Receiving Agent: _____ Date: ___ / ___ / ___ Time: _____

Turned Over By: _____ Date: ___ / ___ / ___ Time: _____

Patient Name: _____ FWSATC Case #: _____

Page 3 of 3   FWSATC

11/13 KT

Appendix B

Nursing Diagnoses
Defined by:
NANDA International, Inc. 2015-2017

Impaired oral mucous membrane
Risk for impaired oral mucous membrane
Impaired tissue integrity
Risk for impaired tissue integrity
Impaired skin integrity
Risk for impaired skin integrity
Risk for urinary tract injury
Acute pain
Risk for constipation
Labile emotional control
Impaired memory (head trauma, hypoxia)
Deficient knowledge
Impaired verbal communication
Risk for compromised human dignity
Disturbed personal identity
Risk for disturbed personal identity
Risk for chronic low self-esteem
Risk for situational low self-esteem
Disturbed body image
Interrupted family processes
Dysfunctional family processes
Risk for ineffective relationship
Post trauma syndrome
Risk for post trauma syndrome
Rape-trauma syndrome
Anxiety
Defensive coping
Ineffective coping
Fear
Powerlessness
Risk for powerlessness

Impaired resilience
Risk for impaired resilience
Moral distress
Spiritual distress
Risk for spiritual distress
Risk for infection
Self-mutilation
Risk for self-mutilation
Risk for suicide

Please note that NANDA International (formerly the North American Nursing Diagnosis Association) lists more than 200 possible nursing diagnoses. Only those most relevant to sexual assault patients are included here.

Appendix C

Resources

The following resources are available for free online:

A National Protocol for Sexual Assault Medical Forensic
Examinations, Adults/Adolescents, Second Edition (April 2013),
from the Department of Justice Office on Violence Against
Women, NCJ 241903
https://www.ncjrs.gov/pdffiles1/ovw/241903.pdf

Evaluation and Management of the Sexually Assaulted or
Sexually Abused Patient, Second Edition, from the American
College of Emergency Physicians. (Sexual Assault eBook)
http://www.acep.org/resources/

Books

Chadwick's Child Maltreatment, Fourth Edition, by David L.
Chadwick, MD, Randell Alexander, MD, PhD, FAAP, Angelo P.
Giardino, MD, PhD, MPH, FAAP, Debra Esernio-Jenssen, MD,
FAAP, Jonathan D. Thackeray, MD, FAAP. Volume 2 of 3:
Sexual Abuse and Psychological Maltreatment (STM
Learning/2014).

*Medical Response to Child Sexual Abuse: A Resource for
Professionals Working with Children and Families* by Rich
Kaplan, MSW, MD, FAAP, Joyce A. Adams, MD, Suzanne P.
Starling, MD, FAAP, Angelo P. Giardino, MD, PhD, MPH,
FAAP (STM Learning/2011).

Journal of Child Sexual Abuse, v20 n5 p481-485 (2011), Special
Issue: Medicine and Child Sexual Abuse: Practices and Innovative
Techniques, Part 1, Randell A. Alexander, Guest Editor.

Peer-Reviewed Articles

Adams JA, Kellogg ND, Farst KJ, Harper NS, Palusci VJ, Frasier LD, Levitt CJ, Shapiro RA, Moles RL, Starling SP, Updated Guidelines for the Medical Assessment and Care of Children Who May Have Been Sexually Abused, *Journal of Pediatric and Adolescent Gynecology* (2015), doi: 10.1016/j.jpag.2015.01.007.

Adams J, Kaplan R, et al: Guidelines for Medical Care of Children who may have been sexually abused. J Pediatr Adolesc Gynecol (2007) 20:163-172

Adams J. Harper K, Adams J, Harper K, Knudson S, et al: Examination findings in legally confirmed cases of child sexual abuse: It's normal to be normal. Pediatrics 1994; 94:310

Adams J: Approach to the interpretation of medical and laboratory findings in suspected child sexual abuse: A 2005 revision. The APSAC Advisor 2005(Summer);7

Adams JA, Botash AS, Kellogg N: Differences in hymenal morphology between adolescent girls with and without a history of consensual sexual intercourse. Arch Pediatr Adolesc Med 2004; 158:280

Anderst J, Kellogg N, et al: Reports of repetitive penile-genital penetration often have no definitive evidence of penetration. Pediatrics 2009; 124: e403-e409. Available: www.pediatrics.org/cgi/doi/10.1542/peds/2008-3053

Berenson AB, Chacko MR, Wiemann CM, et al: A case-control study of anatomic changes resulting from sexual abuse. Am J Obstet Gynecol 2000; 182:820

Berkoff M, Zolotor A, et al: Has this prepubertal girl been sexually abused? JAMA. 2008; 300(23): 2779-2792.

Christian CW, Lavelle JM, De Jong AR, et al: Forensic findings in prepubertal victims of sexual assault. Pediatrics 2000; 106:100

DeLago C, Deblinger E, et al: Girls who disclose sexual abuse: Urogenital symptoms and signs after genital contact. Pediatrics 2008; 122:e281-e286.

Emans SJ, Woods ER, Allred EN, et al: Hymenal findings in

adolescent women: Impact of tampon use and consensual
sexual activity. J Pediatr 1994; 125:153

Finkel M: I can tell you because you're a doctor commentary.
Pediatrics 2008;122:422.

Finkel MA: Anogenital trauma in sexually abused children.
Pediatrics 1989; 84:317

Hammerschlag MR: Sexually transmitted diseases in sexually
abused children: medical and legal implications. Sex Transm
Infect 1998; 74(3):167

Heger A, Emans SJ, Muram D (eds): Evaluation of the Sexually
Abused Child. A Medical Textbook and Photographic Atlas,
(2nd ed.) New York, Oxford University Press, 2000

Heger A, Ticson L,Velasquez O, et al: Children referred for
possible sexual abuse: Medical findings in 2384 children.
Child Abuse Negl 2002; 26:645

Heger AH, Ticson L, Guerra L, et al: Appearance of the genitalia
in girls selected for non-abuse: Review of hymenal
morphology and non-specific findings. J Pediatr Adolesc
Gynecol 2002; 15:27

Heppenstall-Heger A, McConnell G, Ticson L, et al; Healing
patterns in anogenital injuries: A longitudinal study of injuries
associated with sexual abuse, accidental injuries, or genital
surgery in the preadolescent child. Pediatrics 2003; 112:829

Herrmann B, Crawford J: Genital injuries in prepubertal girls
from inline skating accidents. Pediatrics 2002; 110:e16.
Available:
http://www.pediatrics.org/cgi/content/full/110/2/e16.

Hornor G, Scribano P, et al: Emotional response to the anogenital examination of suspected sexual abuse. Journal of
Forensic Nursing 2009 Volume 5 Issue 3, pp 124-130

Hornor G, Scribano, et al: Child sexual assault findings: A
knowledge assessment of sexual assault nurse examiners. The
American Journal for Nurse Practitioners March 2006, vol. 10
No. 3.

Jones JS, Rossman L, Hartman M, et al: Anogenital injuries in
adolescents after consensual sexual intercourse. Acad Emerg
Med 2003; 10:1378

Kellogg N: Clinical report- The evaluation of sexual behaviors in children. Pediatrics Volume 124, Number 3, Sept. 2009.

Kellogg ND, Menard SW, Santos A: Genital anatomy in pregnant adolescents: "normal" doesn't mean "nothing happened". Pediatrics 2004; 223e67. Available: http://www.pediatrics.org/cgi/content/full/113/1/e67.

Kellogg NK and the American Academy of Pediatrics, Committee on Child Abuse and Neglect: Clinical Report: The evaluation of sexual abuse in children. Pediatrics 2005; 116:506

Makoroff K, Brauley J, et al: Genital examinations for alleged sexual abuse of prepubertal girls: findings by pediatric emergency medicine physicians compared with child abuse trained physicians. Child Abuse and Neglect 26 (2002) 1235-1242.

McCann J, Voris J, Simon M, et al: Perianal findings in prepubertal children selected for non-abuse: A descriptive study. Child Abuse Negl 1989; 13:179

McCann J, Voris J, Simon M: Genital injuries resulting from sexual abuse, a longitudinal study. Pediatrics 1992; 89:307

McCann J, Voris J: Perianal injuries resulting from sexual abuse: A longitudinal study. Pediatrics 1993; 91:390

McCann J, Wells R, Simon M, et al: Genital findings in prepubertal girls selected for non-abuse: A descriptive study. Pediatrics 1990; 86:428

Myhre AK, Bemtzen K, Bratlid D: Genital anatomy in non-abused preschool girls. Acta Paediatr 2003; 92:143

Myhre AK, Berntzen K, Bratlid D: Perianal anatomy in nonabused preschool children. Acta Paediatr 2001; 90:1321

Pillai M: Genital findings in prepubertal girls: What can be concluded from an examination? J Pediatr Adolesc Gynecol 2008; 21: 177-185.

UTIs in adolescents; common infections, uncommon challenges. www.contemporarypediatrics.com 2009 Vol. 26, No. 7.

Websites

Childhelp National Child Abuse Hotline: 1-800-4ACHILD
(https://www.childhelp.org)

National Center for Victims of Crime: 1-202-467-8700
 http://www.victimsofcrime.org/

National Coalition Against Domestic Violence: 1-303-839-1852 http://www.ncadv.org/

National Domestic Violence Hotline: 1-800-799-7233 http://www.thehotline.org/

National Human Trafficking Hotline: 1-888-373-7888 or text BeFree (233733) http://www.polarisproject.org/index.php

National Suicide Prevention Lifeline: 1-800-273-8255
http://www.suicidepreventionlifeline.org/

RAINN National Hotline: 1-800-656-HOPE (4673)
https://www.rainn.org/

Safe Helpline: 877-995-5247 https://safehelpline.org/

Enough Abuse Campaign 617-742-8555
http://www.enoughabuse.org/

Appendix D

SAMPLE SANE
Direct Examination Questions

Please tell us your name and spell it for us.
What is your profession?
I want to hand you what's been marked as State's Exhibit ___ for identification (CV). Are you familiar with that document?
What is that?
Does it include all of your training and experience that would be relevant to your testimony here today?
Is all of the information in that document true and correct to the best of your knowledge and belief?
When was it last updated?
This is your current CV?
(MOVE TO ADMIT CV)
I'd like for you to explain briefly all of the letters you have after your name. RN, SANE-A, SANE-P, etc.
What does it stand for?
How long have you held that degree or certification? Specific training?
Specific experience?
Who awarded you that degree or certification? What do you have to do to keep that current?
Do you have other forensic training?
Is that included in your C.V.?
Would you just briefly outline that training for us?
Are you familiar with the term Forensic Nurse Examiner?
What's the difference between FNE and SANE?
Do you belong to any professional organizations?
What is the definition of nursing?
As a nurse are you able to diagnose and treat patients?
What type of diagnosis and treatment are you able to provide?
How is that different from a doctor's diagnosis and treatment?
But both are medical diagnosis and treatment?
Where are you currently employed?

How long have you been employed there?

Where is (employer) located?

What is your specific title/what are your specific job duties at (employer)?

How many examinations have you performed? (adults/children--male/female)

How do you define child/peds?

Do you also review cases/examinations completed by others? Why? How many?

Is there a specific format or procedure that you follow when you perform an examination on a child?

What is that procedure?

Emergency vs. Urgent vs. Non-Urgent--What is the time frame for collecting suspect DNA? What about injury? How long does evidence of injury remain?

Adult v. Ped

Health History (distinguish from Medical History)

Medical History—what is it? What does it include? (symptoms of pain, sensations, inception/general character of cause/external source reasonably pertinent to diagnosis or treatment including recent hygiene activity, methods of concealment, dress, general appearance, impairment due to alcohol or drugs--) Does it include whether or not a girl has started her period? Is that important? Why?

Head-to-toe exam (do you record your observations as you are doing the exam? What types of things do you typically record? How do you record them?)

Genital exam (do you record your observations/what types of things/how/Is the healing process any different for genital injuries than for injuries you would observe in a head-to-toe exam?)

Different procedures for child/adult?

Forensics (describe sex crimes kit/chain-of-custody)

Discharge Plan (patient safety/treatment/counseling options/follow-up care)

Do you have a specific form that you use during each examination to record all of this information? (Pediatric Medical Examination Form)

How many pages is that document? What's on each page?

What specifically do you chart on each page?

Do you ever chart by omission? Explain what that means and what can be inferred

Do you ever do follow-up visits? When/Why?

What do you do on follow-up visit?

Directing your attention to (date of examination). Did you examine a patient by the name of (patient's name)?

What was patient's date of birth?

Was patient able to talk to you and provide information verbally?

What did you tell patient about who you are and what you would be doing?

Did the patient express understanding that you are a nurse?

Where was the physical exam performed?

Who was present?

Who actually performed the sexual assault examination?

Where was (family, friend, detective) during the actual examination?

Did you complete a Medical Forensic Examination Form?

Did you complete that form based upon your own observations?

Do you have that with you today in case you need to use it to refresh your memory?

How did patient present initially (what were your initial observations)?

Did you take a medical history? (Who was present, who asked questions, who provided information?)

What did you observe during your head-to-toe?

Was that consistent with the medical history?

Why or why not?

Did you also perform a genital examination?

Briefly describe the female sex organ for the jury (demonstrative diagram or drawing—mark as exhibit move to admit)

What did you observe during your genital examination?

Were you able to see her hymen?

What did you observe?

What does that mean?

Was that consistent with the medical history?

Why or why not?

(In cases of penetration with no injury) How is that possible?

Did you obtain any forensic specimens?
Did you look for any/swab anywhere?
Why or why not?
Did you make a nursing diagnosis?
What was your diagnosis?
What was your plan of care for this patient?
Did you follow up with this patient?
Why or why not?
Did you do anything further in providing care or treatment for patient?
Are you familiar with the latest research and articles published regarding the sexual abuse of children?
Do you also have substantial training and experience as a medical professional working with child victims of sexual abuse?
What is the frequency of occurrence of injuries in child sexual abuse cases?
What does that mean?

Sample Cross-examination Questions

Ms. Ditton, I noticed that you're on a first name basis with the State, may I also call you Michelle?
The State asked you questions about information you recorded on your Medical Examination Form, is that correct?
That's not the only form you completed, is it?
Isn't it true that you also completed an Application for Benefits form to submit to the Sex Crime Victim Services Fund?
And isn't it also true that you submit that form so that the State can pay you for your services?
And in that form, you identify (patient name) as a victim, don't you?
It's important that you identify her as a victim so that you get paid, isn't it?
And you identify my client as the suspect, don't you?
And you reported that without ever talking to my client, didn't you?

In fact you filled out that form on the same day you examined (patient name), is that correct?

So it wouldn't have mattered to you that my client said this didn't happen? Would it have mattered to you if my client had an alibi? Would it have mattered to you if some other man's DNA were found on (patient)'s body?

Now, you reported sexual trauma to the State, didn't you?

In fact you checked "vaginal", but you've written "FSO" beside it, is that correct?

By FSO did you mean "female sex organ"?

And, isn't it true that you wrote that in because your examination of (patient), didn't reveal any signs of trauma to the vagina, did it?

You didn't believe that anything actually penetrated (patient's) vagina, did you?

(For child-In fact, you never even looked at patient's vagina, did you?)

So you can change the State's form to suit your purpose?

The State expects a licensed physician to sign this form, doesn't it?

But you submitted the form without the signature of a licensed physician, didn't you?

Isn't it true that you just crossed out "physician" and wrote in "SANE-A, SANE-P"?

So again, you changed the form to suit your purpose, didn't you?

So who was it that paid for you to examine (patient)?

I want to look for a moment at page ___ which asks you to diagram the injuries you observed.

I see the words, "no injury noted" is that correct?

And did you write that because you did not observe any injury?

Page 5 of 6 on your chart is a large diagram of the female sex organ, isn't it? And you use that to chart any injury you observe, correct?

So you examined (patient)'s labia majora and found no injury?

And you examined her labia minora and found no injury?

And you examined her perineum and found no injury?

And you examined her clitoris and found no injury?

And you examined her urethra and found no injury?

And you examined her hymen and found no injury?

And you examined her vagina and found no injury?

(Ped-And you didn't bother to look at her vagina, did you? And that's because you knew from what (patient) told you that there wasn't any injury to the vagina?

So you found absolutely no evidence of trauma to (patient)'s female sex organ, is that right?

Yet you reported "vaginal-fso" trauma to the State, didn't you?

Did also examine the patient's anus?

But that's not part of her female sex organ, is it?

And (patient) gave no history involving the anus either, right?

So, you didn't expect to find injury there, either, did you?

And, in fact, you didn't find any injury to (patient)'s anus, did you?

(for child exam page __ of your form you wrote under history, "patient gives history of 1X of breast fondling" Those are your words, not child's, aren't they?

Child never used the word "breast", did she?

And child never used the word "fondle," did she?

In fact, at eight years old, child really doesn't have breasts, does she?

Just so we're clear, all of your findings are consistent with my client's complete denial of what (patient) told you, aren't they?

In other words, it's possible that you found no injury to (patient)'s female sex organ because nobody ever touched her there, isn't it?

Glossary

acquittal – when a defendant is found not guilty of a crime. The opposite of conviction.

advocate – someone who pleads, supports or defends the cause of another, such as a victim advocate or health care advocate.

alternate light source (ALS) – a valuable tool that helps detect forensic evidence (i.e., urine, sweat, semen, saliva, vaginal secretions or fibers) and other substances (i.e., lotion, oils powders) that would otherwise remain invisible to the naked eye. The area fluoresces or glows, allowing potential evidence to be collected, but the collector cannot confirm what the substance or fiber is at the time of collection.

anal fissure - a superficial tear in the lining of the anal canal.

annular hymen – tissue completely surrounds (360°) the vaginal opening; circular, like a ring.

anus - the opening of the rectum from which stool passes, located between the buttocks.

areola: the colored ring around the nipple.

arrest warrant – order signed by a judge finding probable cause that a suspect has committed a crime and should be taken into custody to answer to the charges.

bail – an amount of money paid to the court after arrest but before trial to ensure that the defendant will appear in court as required

beyond a reasonable doubt – the highest level of proof that a crime has been committed, meaning evidence that would firmly convince a reasonable person that there is no credible, non-criminal explanation for the defendant's action.

bond – similar to bail, only the amount of money is secured by property or a bail bond company that charges the defendant a percentage of the bail amount (usually 10%) and guarantees payment in full if the defendant fails to appear in court as required.

buccal swab – cotton swab used to collect cheek cells from inside the mouth for a DNA sample.

burden of proof – in a criminal case, this generally requires the prosecution to prove every element of the charged crime beyond a reasonable doubt. The defendant has no duty to prove or disprove anything unless the defendant raises an affirmative defense such as self-defense, entrapment, alibi or insanity. Then the defendant does have the burden of presenting evidence in support of that defense, but it is a much lower burden of proof. A defendant never has to prove or disprove anything beyond a reasonable doubt. Lesser burdens of proof are clear and convincing evidence (generally applicable in a case involving the termination of parental rights), a preponderance of the evidence (the standard used in civil cases where something must be more likely than not).

Centers for Disease Control and Prevention (CDC) – the CDC's mission is to protect America from health, safety and security threats, both foreign and in the U.S. http://www.cdc.gov/

cervix – the opening of the uterus.

circumstantial evidence – indirect evidence that allows a reasonable person to reach a conclusion. An example of circumstantial evidence is if I wake up in the morning and see that my lawn and driveway are wet. Even though I did not personally observe the rain, I can reasonably infer that it rained absent evidence to the contrary that someone came and hosed down my lawn and driveway or that there is a hidden sprinkler system that operates at night.

clitoral hood - the fold of skin that surrounds and protects the clitoris.

clitoris - small area of erectile tissue that is a source of sexual pleasure in females. Similar to the tissue in the penis.

CODIS - the acronym for the "Combined DNA Index System" and the generic term used to describe the FBI's DNA database.

colposcope - a special instrument that allows any part of the body, including the vagina and cervix to be visualized with increased magnification. Some colposcopes also take photographs.

concurrent sentences – where a defendant has been convicted of multiple crimes and is allowed to serve the sentences simultaneously. For example, if a defendant were convicted and sentenced to 10 years for rape and 10 years for child molesting concurrently, the defendant would be sentenced to serve a total of 10 years.

consecutive sentences – where a defendant has been convicted of multiple crimes and is ordered to serve the sentences one after the other. For example, if a defendant were convicted and sentenced to 10 years for rape and 10 years for child molesting consecutively, the defendant would be sentenced to serve a total of 20 years.

conviction – when a defendant is found guilty of a crime, either by pleading guilty or by a guilty verdict at trial. The opposite of acquittal. A defendant must be convicted of a crime before he or she may be sentenced for a crime.

corroborating evidence - evidence that strengthens or confirms other evidence. A term frequently used when forensic evidence supports a witness's statements.

crescentic hymen – tissue shaped like a crescent moon around the vaginal opening.

cross-examination – questions asked by opposing counsel after the direct examination of a witness. These questions may be leading in a way that only allows the witness to answer yes or no and essentially allows the attorney asking the questions to testify while the witness may only agree or disagree with the information in each question.

cunnilingus – oral sex act on the female genitals.

curriculum vitae (C.V.) – Latin for "course of life," a CV is an overview of a professional's education and training, employment and experience, presentations and publications, and professional memberships. While a resume is often limited to one page and geared toward a single employment objective, a C.V. is more expansive and more frequently updated.

diagnosis (plural-diagnoses) - identification of a disease or condition by a scientific evaluation of physical signs, symptoms, history, laboratory test results, and procedures. Kinds of diagnoses are clinical diagnosis, differential diagnosis, laboratory diagnosis, nursing diagnosis, and physical diagnosis.

differential diagnosis – distinguishing of a particular disease or condition from others that present similar symptoms.

direct examination – questions asked by the attorney who called the witness to the stand to testify. These questions generally must be open-ended, allowing the testimony to come from the witness rather than the attorney.

discovery deposition – a witness's testimony taken before a court reporter in advance of trial to determine how that person is likely to testify at trial. Opposing counsel must be present and also have the opportunity to ask questions of the witness.

double jeopardy – 5th amendment protection that prohibits a person from being tried twice for the same crime.

due process – 5th and 14th Amendment right that requires federal and state government to treat people with fundamental fairness.

exculpatory evidence – evidence that exonerates a person or tends to prove a defendant's innocence.

evidentiary deposition – a witness's testimony given before a court reporter in order to be used as evidence at trial because the witness is unavailable to testify in person at trial. Opposing counsel must be present and have the opportunity to cross-examine the witness.

fellatio – oral sex act on the male genitals.

female sex organ (FSO) - A legal term, not a medical term for the female genitals.

fimbriated hymen – tissue has many projections which give it a ruffled appearance surrounding the vaginal opening.

floating with saline - a technique using saline to better visualize the hymen where drops of saline are placed at the tip of the clitoral hood and run down into the labia. The labia are then rubbed together gently to open an estrogenized hymen that is stuck together so that the hymenal ring may be fully visualized. .

Foley catheter- a thin, sterile, flexible tube used to drain urine from the bladder. In post-perbertal children or women, it is used as a tool to check for injury to the hymenal rim by inserting the balloon tip into the vagina, inflating it with air and pulling gently outward to assess the hymenal ring.

fossa navicularis – the concave area between the posterior fourchette and the hymen.

frog-leg position – a position used with small children during the sexual assault examination where the child lies on her back, raises her knees to her chest, and then spreads her legs by putting the soles of her feet together.

goose lamp – an electric lamp with a flexible shaft that permits control of the direction of light.

hearsay – a statement made by someone outside of the courtroom who is not available for cross-examination and the statement is being offered to prove that what was said is true. Hearsay is generally not admissible as evidence, but there are many exceptions to this rule (such as Medical Hearsay Exception) where the statement is considered reliable enough to be allowed.

hematoma - a collection of blood outside of a blood vessel.

hymen- a collar or semicollar of tissue that surrounds the vaginal opening, The hymen DOES NOT cover the vaginal opening or act as a seal.

imperforate – used to describe a hymen with no opening. This is very rare and requires medical attention.

introitus (hymenal orifice) - the opening in the middle of the hymen. Objects entering the vagina first pass through the introitus.

initial plea – in a serious felony case, the court will enter an initial plea of not guilty to all of the criminal charges to ensure that the defendant has adequate opportunity to consult with an attorney before entering a formal plea of guilty or setting the case for trial.

knee chest – position where patient is face down and rests on the knees and upper part of the chest. Used to visualize the anus, and the female sex organ.

labia majora- the two outer folds (lips) of adipose tissue. May be covered with course pubic hair.

labia minora- the two inner folds (lips) of tissue, between the labia majora and the hymenal ring, and within the vulva.

labial adhesions - the fusion of the labia minora. Fusion may occur at any point and be minimal or involve all the tissue.

LGBT/Queer – LGBT stands for lesbian, gay, bisexual, transgender. This acronym is evolving, and the term "queer" is sometimes used as an umbrella term for the entire group. The current full acronym is LGBTQIAP for lesbian, gay, bisexual, transgender, queer, intersex, asexual, pansexual.

lithotomy – a position used during examinations in which the patient is on her back with feet above or at the level of the hips with feet in stirrups and with the patient's perineum at the edge of the exam table.

median raphe (perineal raphe) – the midline fusion or ridge of tissue that extends up from the anus and marks the line of union of the two halves of the perineum. Some are prominent, especially on men, others are barely noticeable. A completely normal finding for both men and women that may be confused for scars by the untrained observer.

medical - of or connected with medicine or the practice or study of medicine.

medical hearsay exception – medical providers may testify to statements their patients made to them for the purpose of diagnosis and treatment.

medicine -the science and art of treating, curing and preventing disease, relieving pain, and improving and preserving health.

Miranda warnings – the constitutional rights that must be explained to a suspect in custody before interrogation according to the U.S. Supreme Court Case *Miranda v. Arizona*, 386 U.S. 436 (1966); specifically, that the person has the right to remain silent, that anything he says may be used against him in a court of law, that he has the right to consult with an attorney, and if he cannot afford an attorney one will be appointed for him.

mons pubis – mound of fatty tissue where pubic hair grows.

motion in limine - a motion filed by attorneys on either side prior to trial in order to get an advance ruling from the judge as to whether or not certain evidence should be admitted at trial. An attorney seeking to exclude evidence will argue that it is inadmissible under the rules or evidence or that it is unfairly prejudicial. An attorney seeking to introduce the evidence at trial will argue that it is admissible under an exception to the general rule or that its probative value outweighs any unfair prejudice.

motion to suppress – a motion filed by a defendant alleging that the police obtained evidence in violation of his constitutional rights and asking the judge not to permit the prosecution to present that evidence at trial.

National Crime Victim Survey (NCVS) – an annual survey of random households conducted by the Bureau of Justice Statistics to provide data on crimes that have affected each household. The NCVS is the primary source of information on victimization in the USA. http://www.bjs.gov/

nursing - the protection, promotion and optimization of health and abilities, prevention of illness and injury, alleviation of suffering through the diagnosis and treatment of human response, and advocacy in the care of individuals, families, communities, and populations (as defined by the American Nurses Association's Nursing Scope & Standards of Practice).

objection – how an attorney alerts the judge to a potentially improper question asked of a witness. Common objections include that the question calls for hearsay, is argumentative, assumes a fact not in evidence or is leading (only during direct examination).

objection overruled – the judge allows the question and the witness must answer it.

objection sustained – the judge agrees that the question is improper so the witness is not required to answer it.

papilla - the small projecting part at the center of the nipple

patient - a recipient of a health care service.

pediatrician - a medical doctor who manages the physical, behavioral, and mental health of children from birth through young adulthood (usually until age 18 or 21).

perineum - the external surface between the female sex organ and the anus in females, and the scrotum and anus in males.

petechiae - pinpoint, round spots that appear on the skin as a result of bleeding under the skin.

plea agreement (or plea bargain or plea deal) – when a defendant agrees to plead guilty to some or all of the charges in exchange for the dismissal of other charges or a specific sentence within the controlling sentencing guidelines.

plead "straight up" – when a defendant pleads guilty to all of the criminal charges with no plea agreement, leaving sentencing entirely up to the court.

posterior fourchette – the area of mucosal skin where the labia minora meet (opposite end from the clitoral hood).

prepubescent – before puberty

prepuce (foreskin) – tissue that covers the glans in uncircumcised males. The prepuce is removed during circumcision.

probable cause – where the facts and circumstances would lead a reasonable person to believe that a particular person has committed a particular crime or that particular evidence of a crime may be found in a particular place.

probative value – the extent to which any piece of evidence or testimony serves to prove a specific fact relevant to any element of the crime or issue in the case.

prone – lying face down.

prosecuting attorney – an attorney who represents the state or federal government by filing charges and proving that a defendant has violated the relevant criminal code.

q-tip - a wooden stick with cotton on the end. Two q-tips are used in evidence collection.

Rape, Abuse & Incest National Network (RAINN) - the USA's largest anti-sexual violence organization. https://www.rainn.org/

rape shield laws – laws designed to protect victims from embarrassment and victim-blaming by prohibiting the introduction of evidence about the victim's sexual life with anyone other than the defendant. Specific rules on what is permitted vary from state to state.

rectum- The distal portion of the large intestine, ending at the anal canal. (Inside the patient; can't see)

search warrant – order signed by a judge finding probable cause to believe that specific evidence of a crime may be found in a specific place and authorizing police to search that place and seize the evidence.

sentence – the lawful sanction imposed by the court on a defendant convicted of violating the criminal law. Typical sentences may include fines, restitution, incarceration, rehabilitative services, and probation.

separation - examiner uses gloved hands to separate labia majora and labia minora to assess the inside of the FSO.

sex offender registry – a tool for identifying and tracking people convicted of sex crimes. Operated by the Department of Justice, the National Sex Offender Public Website (NSOPW) is the only U.S. government website that links public state, territorial, and tribal sex offender registries. http://www.nsopw.gov/en.

statutory rape - sexual intercourse or penetration with a person under the legal age of consent.

speculum – a metal or plastic instrument inserted into the vagina during a gynecological exam to facilitate visualization or swabbing of the cervix.

subpoena – a court order requiring a witness to attend a deposition or hearing or trial. Attorneys who represent a party to the case are able to act as an officer of the court and issue subpoenas compelling witnesses to attend and testify.

subpoena duces tecum – a subpoena that requires a witness to bring certain documents or evidence to a deposition, hearing or trial.

supine – position where the patient is lying face up with her back against the bed or examination table.

Tanner scale – stages of physical development for children, adolescents and adults created by the British pediatrician James Tanner.

testicles (testes) - the two egg-shaped glands inside the scrotum that produce testosterone and sperm.

Toludine blue - a blue dye that can show injury to tissue that would not be visible to the "naked" eye or without magnification.

traction - the examiner uses gloved hands to hold the labia and pull down and toward the examiner to assess further into the FSO.

Uniform Crime Reports (UCR) – an annual summary of the crimes reported to the police and arrests made in the USA tallied by the FBI based on data submitted by individual police departments. http://www.fbi.gov/stats-services/crimestats

urethral meatus - the opening from which urine passes.

uterus – the muscular, pear-shaped organ where an embryo develops, also known as the womb.

vagina – the birth canal.

vaginal opening - the opening to the birth canal.

vascular – having many blood vessels.

vas deferens: - the tube in male anatomy that connects the testes with the urethra.

vestibule - the space between the labia minora into which the urethra and vagina open. (A space or a cavity that serves as the entrance to a passageway.)

victim - one that is subjected to oppression, hardship, or mistreatment. One who suffers injury, loss, or death as a result of another person's actions.

voir dire – the jury selection process before a trial begins during which a panel of potential jurors answer questions posed by the court or the attorneys for both parties to determine their fitness to serve as a juror. The Latin term *voir dire* literally means to tell the truth.

vulva – the external, visible part of the female genitalia including the labia majora, labia minora, clitoral hood, clitoris, and the vaginal opening.

vulvar coitus - Rubbing of the penis between the labia without entering the vagina.

About the Authors

Michelle Ditton RN, SANE-A, SANE-P

Michelle is the Chief Nursing Officer/Executive Director, and one of the founders of the Fort Wayne Sexual Assault Treatment Center which began operations in 1996. As a graduate of Purdue University, Michelle has been an RN for 35 years with clinical experience in the emergency room, neonatal intensive care unit, and pediatrics to name a few. The past 20 years of her nursing career have been in the field of forensic nursing. She received her adult and adolescent sexual assault didactic and clinical training at Pomerado Hospital in San Diego, California. In 2002, the IAFN offered the first adult/adolescent sexual assault nurse examiner certification examination, at which time Michelle obtained her board certification.

During 1998 thru 2000, Michelle received her pediatric sexual assault training with seven mini fellowships across the country with leaders in the field of sexual assault. She spent over 2,400 hours in advanced training. She used this knowledge to develop the pediatric sexual assault program from within the SATC. She helped establish the Dr. Bill Lewis Center for Children with fellow community leaders which opened its doors in June 2000. In 2007, the IAFN first offered the certification exam for pediatric sexual assault nurse examiners and Michelle obtained her board certification at that time.

Michelle has facilitated in the revisions of all policies concerning sexual assault for Parkview Health Systems and Lutheran Health Network, and the procedures currently implemented in all local hospitals. She serves on the guideline committee for the State of Indiana to produce the "Indiana Statewide Guidelines for Sexual Assault Response Teams. Michelle is a recognized speaker and trainer at the local, state and national levels. Michelle is responsible for training 2nd year family practice residents, IU medical students, and the local ER staff in Fort Wayne, IN. She serves as a consultant for Fox Valley Technical College and has taught for the Office of Juvenile Justice and Delinquency Prevention (OJJDP). She has also served as faculty for the past 6 years at the National Symposium on Child Abuse in Huntsville, Alabama. Michelle is also the professional contributor to the International Association of Forensic Nurses (IAFN) Pediatric Guidelines (Review and Revisions Committee, 2008), and to the IAFN 2012 Intimate Partner Violence Education Guidelines.

Michelle has been published and contributed to numerous articles including being a co-author for the article "Veracity for Children in Pediatric Forensics" in the peer-reviewed *Journal of Forensic Nursing,* which was released on-line June 19, 2012. This article "Veracity for Children in Pediatric Forensics" was also chosen, published and reviewed in *The Quarterly Update,* Volume XX, Number 3. She is the co-contributor with Julie Kenniston, MSW, LSW, "Sexual Abuse Issues Related to Interviewing Children," Chapter 2 in Volume 2 of the 4th Edition Chadwick Child Maltreatment Encyclopedia three volume series. Michelle also co-contributes with Laurie Gray, JD for a Q&A Medical-Legal Column, "Legally SANE" in the quarterly newsletter "The Examiner" for members of the Indiana Chapter of the IAFN and ENA.

Laurie A. Gray, JD

Laurie writes based upon her experience as an educator, attorney, and child forensic interviewer. She earned her B.A. from Goshen College in 1986 and her J.D. from Indiana University Maurer School of Law in 1993. From 1986-1990 Laurie taught high school Spanish, coaching volleyball, basketball and academic teams, and working summers as an interpreter for a missionary group in Guatemala. An experienced civil and criminal trial attorney, Laurie joined the Allen County Indiana Prosecuting Attorney's Office in February of 2000 as a full-time deputy assigned to Felony Sex Crimes. After an extended maternity leave, Laurie returned to work as a part-time deputy prosecutor assigned to the Drug Court Intervention Program and Juvenile Sex Offenses through April of 2010.

Laurie has served as an author and lecturer for various Indiana Continuing Legal Education programs, a co-chair of the Women Lawyers Section of the Allen County Bar Association and court-appointed guardian *ad litem* in child welfare cases, and court-appointed Spanish/English interpreter in both state and federal courts. Laurie served on the faculty at the National Symposium on Child Abuse in Huntsville, Alabama, every spring from 2009 - 2014. She also works as an adjunct professor of criminal sciences at Indiana Institute of Technology (Indiana Tech) and as a bilingual Forensic Interviewer at the Dr. Bill Lewis Center for Children in Fort Wayne, Indiana, conducting interviews in both Spanish and English. In 2014, Laurie was appointed to serve a four-year term as the Victim Advocate on the Allen County Indiana Community Corrections Board.

Laurie is the founder and president of Socratic Parenting, LLC (www.SocraticParenting.com), and the author of four other books. Her debut novel *Summer Sanctuary* (Luminis Books / 2010), won a Moonbeam Gold Medal for excellence in young adult fiction and was named a 2011 Indiana Best Book Finalist. Laurie's second young adult novel *Maybe I Will* is also a Moonbeam Medalist and a 2014 YALSA Teens' Top Ten Nominee. Luminis Books released Laurie's novel set in ancient Greece, *Just Myrto*, and her parenting book, *A Simple Guide to Socratic Parenting*, in 2014.

Laurie was part of the first multi-disciplinary team (MDT) from Allen County, Indiana, to attend the Childhood Trust forensic interviewing training in Cincinnati, Ohio, in March of 2000 in anticipation of opening a Child Advocacy Center (now the Dr. Bill Lewis Center for Children) in Fort Wayne, Indiana, in June of 2000. She has been part of the MDT since 2000, first as a deputy prosecutor attending interviews and reviewing recorded interviews for charging purposes and now as a child forensic interviewer.

IF YOU'VE BEEN SEXUALLY ASSAULTED

1. Get to a safe place, away from the assailant.
2. Call 911.
3. Preserve evidence (Don't urinate, douche, bathe, brush your teeth, wash your hands, change clothes, or eat or drink anything)
4. Request a rape kit examination.
5. If you suspect you were drugged, ask that a urine sample be collected.

If you are an adult and choose not to report the assault to the police, you should still seek medical attention to determine the risk of sexually transmitted infections and pregnancy.

For more information, visit the Rape, Abuse & Incest National Network online at www.RAINN.org or call the National Sexual Assault Hotline for free, confidential counseling, 24 hours a day: 1-800-656-HOPE (4673). It's never too late to ask for help!

National Resources:

Childhelp National Child Abuse Hotline: 1-800-4ACHILD
(https://www.childhelp.org)
National Center for Victims of Crime: 1-202-467-8700
 http://www.victimsofcrime.org/
National Coalition Against Domestic Violence: 1-303-839-1852 http://www.ncadv.org/
National Domestic Violence Hotline: 1-800-799-7233
http://www.thehotline.org/
National Human Trafficking Hotline: 1-888-373-7888 or text
BeFree (233733) http://www.polarisproject.org/index.php
National Suicide Prevention Lifeline: 1-800-273-8255
http://www.suicidepreventionlifeline.org/
RAINN National Hotline: 1-800-656-HOPE (4673)
https://www.rainn.org/
Safe Helpline: 877-995-5247 https://safehelpline.org/
Enough Abuse Campaign 617-742-8555
http://www.enoughabuse.org/

Made in United States
North Haven, CT
10 April 2024

51159176R00095